APPLIED MECHANICS

(S.I. Units)

by

A. W. FINLAYSON, B.Sc.

and

D. J. McALPINE, Dip.Ed.H., H.N.C.

HOLMES – McDOUGALL LTD.
EDINBURGH

First Edition	1962.
Revised Edition	1964.
Third Edition	1967.
Revised Edition S.I. Units	1969.

PRINTED BY GEORGE OUTRAM & CO. LTD., 22 UNION ROW, ABERDEEN.

PREFACE

It has been the express intention of the authors to keep the language of the book and the explanation of facts as simple as possible without belittling the subject matter. The mathematics used in the various calculations should not present any great difficulty and in many cases, especially in the earlier chapters, graphical solutions will suffice.

Each chapter is complete in itself so that study may commence at whichever chapter the class teacher chooses and an adequate number of problems are included at the end of each chapter.

The introduction of S.I. units leads to a different treatment of the subject matter from previously but, as yet, many details of the work have not been definitely settled. e.g. The spelling of kilogram (me) is optional but it is assumed that the engineering industry will use kilogram. The value of 'g' is almost universally taken to be 9.81 although in some quarters 10 is taken as an acceptable approximation.

It is essential that before the system can be fully appreciated we must not be tempted to convert, either mentally or physically, S.I. dimensions into imperial dimensions or vice versa.

The authors wish to thank Mr. A. W. Gordon, B.SC., and Mr. F. Philip Kitchen, M.A., both of Coatbridge High School, for their very careful and critical reading of the original manuscript.

A. W. FINLAYSON
D. J. MCALPINE

GLASGOW,
July, 1969.

CONTENTS

CHAPTER I

FORCE

APPLIED MECHANICS

Mechanics is the branch of science that deals with the behaviour of matter under the action of force.

Mechanics can be divided into dynamics, which deals with the movement of bodies and the forces which cause that movement, and statics, in which the body remains at rest under the action of forces.

Force

Before we can study mechanics we must know exactly what a force is, and what it does. Now you know that if you give anything a push or a pull you are exerting a force on it. If you give the object a very light push your force will tend to make it move, but it might not succeed. If you push hard enough you will make the object move.

Forces do not always make things move, however; sometimes they do exactly the opposite and stop things moving. A motor car may be moving at 50 km/h when the driver applies the brakes. The brakes exert a force on the wheels which stops them moving, and so stops the car. Thus the car, in a state of motion, is brought to rest by the force.

Sometimes the force does not assist or hinder motion. Imagine a boat crossing a river. It sets out to cross directly to the other side, but when it reaches the centre of the stream, the current exerts a force which carries the boat downstream. The engine still drives the boat forward but the force of the current alters the direction of motion of the boat.

Now in all these cases we can see the action of different forces and they all have one thing in common—each force changes (or tries to change) the motion of the body on which it acts.

This then is how we describe a force.

A force is that which changes, or tends to change, a body's state of rest or motion.

Types of force

There are many types of force and you will probably be able to think of half a dozen different forces without any difficulty. Among them might be the force exerted by a railway engine pulling a train, the force which the wind exerts on the sails of a ship or which water exerts to

1

turn a water wheel, the force required to stretch a spring (or to compress it), the force required to lift a stone, a brick, etc. Let us examine
some of these forces in more detail.

Mass and weight

The brick mentioned in the last paragraph consists of a lump of
clay pressed into a shape and heated until the clay 'fires' and becomes
the brick as we know it. Now, there is a certain amount of material
(clay) in the brick and no matter where you take the brick or what you
do with it, unless you break it and take away some of the material, the
amount of matter is unaltered. You might set the brick on the table,
you might build it into a wall, you might take it to Africa or the North
Pole, you might take it down a pit or up in an aeroplane or you might
fire it by rocket into outer space, but whatever you do, unless you
remove some of the material of the brick, the original amount of
matter will still be there. This amount of matter is known as the mass
of the brick and as long as the amount of matter in it remains constant,
the mass of the brick remains constant.

Now let us examine the brick as it lies on the ground. If we lift the
brick upwards through a height of, say, one metre from the ground,
we have to exert a force on the brick to move it and to hold it in position.
If we let it go it moves towards the earth and, as it requires a force to
make anything move, there must be a force acting on the body. This
force is, of course, the force of gravity on the brick or the weight of the
brick.

Relationship between mass and weight

We have seen that we require a certain force to lift a brick, i.e. a
certain force to lift the amount of matter that is contained in the brick.
Obviously if we try to lift two identical bricks we will have twice the
amount of matter and will require twice the amount of force. For
three bricks we would need three times the force and the more bricks
we wanted to lift, i.e. the greater the mass of bricks then the greater
would be the force required. In other words, as the mass of material
gets greater its weight gets correspondingly greater, or, if we want to
be more scientific, the weight of the material is proportional to its
mass. This is an important fact and is commonly used to determine
the mass of any body.

Finding the mass of a body

Always, when we are comparing objects, we have to describe one in
terms of the other and when we have a lot of objects to compare we
can take one and describe the others in terms of it. In finding the mass
of a body we compare it with the standard unit of mass and this
standard unit of mass is the International Prototype Kilogramme
which is the mass of a certain cylinder of platinum irridium kept at

the International Bureau of Weights and Measures at Sevres near Paris. There is no really convenient way of comparing masses directly but if we remember that the mass of any body is proportional to its weight then we can use this fact to compare weights and therefore compare masses. For this we use the beam balance and put the standard mass in one pan and load the other pan with, say, sand. When the pans balance then the gravitational pull on the sand balances the gravitational pull on the standard mass and since these forces are equal then the masses themselves must be equal. In this way we can compare other masses with the standard kilogramme.

Measurement of force

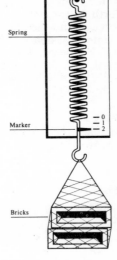

We know that it requires a force to stretch or compress a spring and the effect of various forces on a spring can be seen by hanging a spring on a nail as shown in Fig. 1. Mark the original length of the spring and then place a brick in the net bag. Mark the extension caused by the weight of the brick, i.e. by one unit of force. Place another brick in the bag and again mark the extension. Repeat this with 3, 4, 5 bricks and then examine the spacing of the marks. Since each brick has the same weight each will exert the same force on the spring and it will be seen that the addition of equal weights (or forces) causes the spring to extend by equal amounts. This is the principle on which the spring balance works and in the commercially manufactured spring balance the scale of the balance is marked off in units of force called **newtons.**

Ask your teacher for a spring balance of either the compression or tension type

Fig. 1

and push or pull it until the scale shows a reading of one newton. Try it at 2, 3, 5, 10 and 20 newtons just to get the 'feel' of the forces involved. Try also weighing various bodies (your brick, for instance) and get the force, in newtons with which the earth attracts them.

Weight of one kilogram mass

Using a spring balance graduated in newtons, find the weight of a mass of one kilogram. Note the result very carefully as you will require to use this value very often in the future. If your balance is very accurate and you take the reading carefully you will find that one kilogram mass has a weight of 9·81 newtons. Later when you study dynamics you will find out more about this number 9·81, but in the meantime we will use it and in our work we will denote it by the letter 'g'.

It should be pointed out, however, that the weight of a body is not an absolute figure and varies slightly depending on the place in which the body is weighed. A body weighed on a spring balance at the north or south poles would be slightly heavier than if it were weighed at the equator and a body weighed up in an aeroplane or down a deep pit would be slightly lighter than if weighed at the earth's surface. However, these variations are very slight and in our work we will ignore them.

Representation of the force on a body due to gravity

The force on a body due to gravity may be represented in various ways, for example, as F_g, meaning the force, in newtons, with which the earth pulls the body. Notice in this case that $_g$ is a suffix describing the force F. In other cases this force, since it is the weight of the body, may simply be denoted by the letter W. Another way to refer to this force is by the product of the mass and 'g'. For example, the pull of the earth on a body of mass $m = mg$ newtons. Note that in this case 'g' is the figure 9·81 and mg means the product of the mass and 9·81.

Be prepared to meet this force described in any of the above ways.

Example 1

Calculate the force with which the earth attracts a mass of 3 kg (i.e. the weight of a 3 kg mass).

$$\text{Force due to gravity } (F_g) = 3 \times 9\cdot81$$
$$= \mathbf{29\cdot43} \text{ newtons}$$

Example 2

A mass of 5 kg is hung on the end of a rope. Calculate the pull on the rope.

$$\text{Pull on the rope} = \text{weight of the 5 kg mass}$$
$$= mg$$
$$= 5 \times 9\cdot81$$
$$= \mathbf{49\cdot05 \ N}$$

Action and reaction

In our definition we defined a single force, but careful consideration will show that a single force can never exist. Forces must always occur in pairs. This is easily seen if you try to push a heavy load while standing on a slippy surface; you try to push the load but your feet slip in the opposite direction. You can only exert a strong force on the load if your feet can exert an equal force acting in the opposite direction on the ground.

Similarly, when you lift a load your feet exert a force on the ground in the opposite direction to the lifting force which you apply to the load.

If a heavy iron mass rests on the ground (Fig. 2), the weight of the iron (i.e. the force on the iron due to gravity), exerts a force of mg newtons on the surface of the ground. Since the iron is at rest, this force must be balanced by an equal force R N exerted by the ground on the iron. This force R is known as a **reaction,** and a reaction is always brought into play when a force acts against a rigid body. The reaction on the body is always equal in magnitude to the force but it acts in the opposite direction.

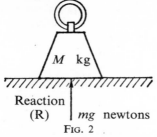

Reaction
(R) mg newtons
Fig. 2

Reactions occur, for example, when a mass hangs on a rope from a roof, when a ladder rests against a wall, when a boat pulls at its moorings, etc.

Representation of a force

In order to describe a force completely there are several things we must know about it. We must know its size or **magnitude.** For our purposes we measure magnitude in newtons.

We must also know the **direction** in which the force acts, since this will affect the motion of the body on which it is acting. For example, a cyclist goes much faster with the wind behind him than he does with the wind in his face.

A third thing that can affect the motion of the body is the **point of application** of the force. For example, if we take a long piece of wood standing on end and apply a sudden force at the top (as shown at A, Fig. 3) the wood is knocked over.

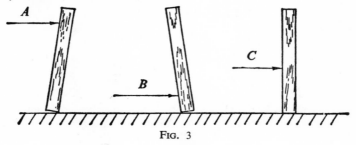

Fig. 3

If the same force is applied at B it knocks the bottom of the wood away so that it falls backwards in the opposite direction, and if it is applied at C the wood is knocked bodily to the side.

So that in order to define a force completely we need to know:—

(1) its magnitude;
(2) its direction or line of action;
(3) its point of application.

We can represent a force on paper by a straight line. The length of the line, drawn to scale, represents the magnitude of the force; the direction of the line shows the direction of the force, and an arrow head shows the sense of direction. The point of application is shown by the end of the line.

For example

The line *AB* (Fig. 4), being 8 cm long, represents a force of 40 N acting in the direction of the line, and the point of application is at *B*.

Scale: 1 cm rep. 5 N

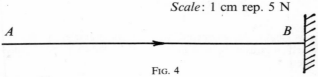

FIG. 4

Vector quantities

A quantity, such as force, that has direction as well as magnitude is known as a **vector** quantity. Other vector quantities are velocity and acceleration.

A quantity that has magnitude but no direction is known as a **scalar** quantity. Examples of scalar quantities are 5 pencils, 6 apples, etc.

Equilibrium

If a force of 2 newtons is applied to a point *P* at rest, the point will start to move under the action of the force (Fig. 5a).

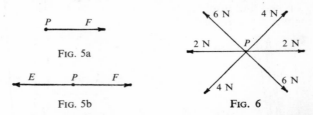

FIG. 5a

FIG. 5b

FIG. 6

If two forces *E* and *F*, both of 2 N, are applied to the point at the same time so that they act in opposite directions, the forces will balance and the point will remain at rest. When the forces acting at a point balance like this, we say that the point is in **equilibrium** (Fig. 5b).

You will easily see that the point *P* (Fig. 6) is also in equilibrium although there are six forces acting on it.

If these six forces had suddenly been applied while the point was at rest, it would have remained at rest. But if the point had been moving when they were applied it would have kept on moving at the same speed and in the same direction and still have been in equilibrium, i.e. the point can be in equilibrium if it is at rest or if it is moving with constant speed in a straight line. You will meet this second condition of equilibrium later when studying friction.

Resultant

If two men, each exerting a force of 100 N, push a truck against a resistance of 50 N the truck will gain speed. Obviously the same effect would be obtained if the three forces, i.e. the two men and the resistance could be replaced by one force of 150 N acting in the direction in which the men were pushing. This 150 N force is known as the **resultant** of the other three forces.

FIG. 7 FIG. 8

The resultant of several forces is that single force which acting alone would have the same effect as the given forces.

In this case the lines of action of the forces are parallel, but the same conditions apply when the forces are inclined to each other.

Figure 8 shows two tugs pulling a liner. The two hawsers exert forces on the liner each of which tends to pull it off course, but as they act together they pull it along its correct course.

The two tugs exerting forces *A* and *B* could be replaced by a single tug exerting a force *R* and the same effect would be obtained. In this case force *R* is the resultant of forces *A* and *B*.

Equilibrant

If several forces act at a point they can generally be replaced by a single force—their resultant. Now if we put another force into the system equal in magnitude to the resultant but acting in the opposite direction, this new force will balance the system, i.e. it will bring it into equilibrium. This force is known as the **equilibrant.**

The equilibrant of a system of several forces is that force which will balance the system or bring it into equilibrium.

N.B.—The equilibrant and the resultant always act in the same straight line and are always equal in magnitude but opposite in direction.

STATICS

If one force acts on a point at rest, it causes the point to move, i.e. the point cannot be in equilibrium.

If two forces act on a point, the point will be in equilibrium if the forces are equal in magnitude but opposite in direction.

Now let us consider three forces **in one plane** acting on a body in equilibrium. The lines of action of the forces may be **parallel** or **non-parallel**.

(1) Parallel coplanar forces

The body may be in equilibrium under the action of three forces if the lines of action of the forces are parallel. Figure 9 shows an example of a body in equilibrium under the action of three parallel coplanar forces.

We shall deal more fully with this case when studying the moments of forces.

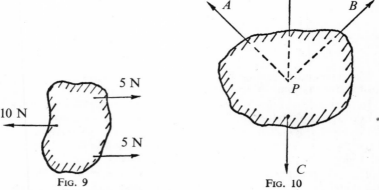

FIG. 9   FIG. 10

(2) Non-parallel coplanar forces

Let us suppose three forces A, B, and C act on an irregular body and produce equilibrium (Fig. 10).

If we produce the lines of action of forces A and B backwards they will meet at point P so that the resultant R of forces A and B must pass through point P.

In order to produce equilibrium the resultant R must be equal and opposite to force C, i.e. force C must pass through point P. The three forces must therefore be concurrent.

$N.B.$—If three forces acting at a point are to produce equilibrium they must all act in the same plane. If one of the forces acts out of the plane formed by the other two, then the forces cannot produce equilibrium.

Thus we see that a system of three forces can only be in equilibrium if
(1) the forces are coplanar;
(2) the lines of action of the forces are parallel or concurrent.

The triangle of forces

The theorem known as "the triangle of forces" states:—

If three forces acting at a point are in equilibrium they can be represented in magnitude and direction by the sides of a triangle taken in order.

We can verify the theorem by the following experiment.

Experiment 1

Object: To verify the triangle of forces.

Apparatus: We require a drawing-board fixed vertically to the wall, a sheet of drawing-paper, two free-running pulleys, string, a supply of masses, a set square, and a rule.

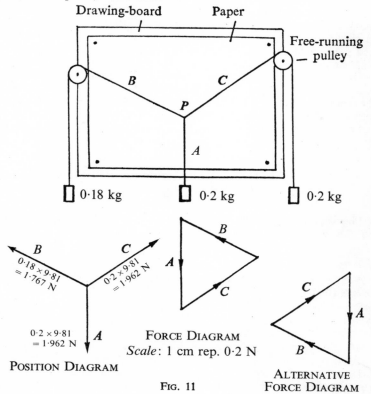

FIG. 11

Procedure: Pin the sheet of drawing-paper to the board and fasten two pulleys to the edges of the board as shown. Tie three pieces of string at a common point, tie a mass to each of the free ends, hang two of the strings over the pulleys and allow the system to come to rest, taking care that none of the masses is rubbing against the wall or the board. If the system does not come to rest with point *P* on the paper alter the sizes of the masses or the position of the pulleys until it does.

Mark the position of point *P* on the paper. Calculate the magnitudes and mark the lines of action of forces *A, B,* and *C.* Remove the masses and pulleys and take the drawing-paper from the board.

On the paper is marked the common point and the magnitudes and directions of the three forces. Such a drawing is known as a **space or position diagram** since it gives the positions of all the members of the system.

On a clear part of the paper, using the rule and set square, draw a line parallel to the line of action of force *A.* Choose a suitable scale, mark off force *A* to scale on the line and insert an arrow on the line to show the direction of the force. From the end of line *A* draw a line parallel to the line of action of force *B* and mark off force *B* to scale on this line as shown in Fig. 11. Follow line *B* with a line parallel to the line of action of force *C.* Mark off the magnitude and direction of force *C* on this line. You will find that the end of line *C* finished at the beginning of line *A* forming a triangle and that the direction arrows follow each other round the triangle.

This diagram, where the forces are represented to scale, is known as the force diagram. Since a force is a vector it is, in fact, a vector diagram.

N.B.—By taking the forces in a different order when transferring them from the position diagram to the force diagram an alternative triangle of forces can be obtained.

The triangle of forces is very useful in finding unknown forces in ropes, wires, beams, etc.

Example 1

A mass of 70 kg is hung on a rope. Find the force required to deflect the rope to an angle of 30° from the vertical.

Draw the position diagram showing the mass and the ropes exerting forces on it. Calculate the force of gravity (*mg*) acting on the body, i.e. its weight. Name all the forces (Fig. 12).

We can represent the weight (*mg*) of the load in magnitude and direction since we know both of these. We do not know the magnitudes of forces *D* and *R*, but knowing their directions we can complete the triangle of forces and find the point where they meet. From the force

diagram the lengths of lines *D* and *R* give the magnitudes to scale of
the deflecting force and the force in the rope.

By measurement: $D = 3\cdot96$ cm   Deflecting force $= 396$ N
                  $R = 7\cdot9$ cm   Force in rope $= 790$ N

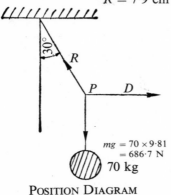

$mg = 70 \times 9\cdot81$
$\quad\;\; = 686\cdot7$ N
70 kg

POSITION DIAGRAM

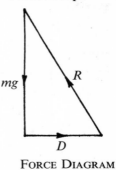

FORCE DIAGRAM
Scale: 1 cm rep. 100 N

FIG. 12

Example 2

A beam 3 m long is slung from a crane hook by two rope slings
each 2 m long, fastened at the ends of the beam. If the mass of the beam
is 50 kg find the tension in each of the slings.

We need to draw the position diagram to get the relative positions
of all the forces. Choose a suitable scale and draw the beam to scale
(Fig. 13). Using compasses, draw the slings to scale and so find the
position of the crane hook. We now have three forces acting at the
crane hook and since the total weight of the beam is carried by the crane
rope we can calculate the magnitude and we know the direction of
the force in the rope. This enables us to draw the triangle of forces for
the three forces acting at the hook *H*.

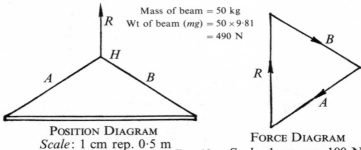

Mass of beam $= 50$ kg
Wt of beam (mg) $= 50 \times 9\cdot81$
$\qquad\qquad = 490$ N

POSITION DIAGRAM
Scale: 1 cm rep. 0·5 m

FORCE DIAGRAM
Scale: 1 cm rep. 100 N

FIG. 13

Force in each sling $= 370$ N

Example 3

A wall crane (Fig. 14) has a jib 3 m long and a horizontal tie 2 m long. Find the force in the jib and tie when the crane is carrying a load of 120 kg.

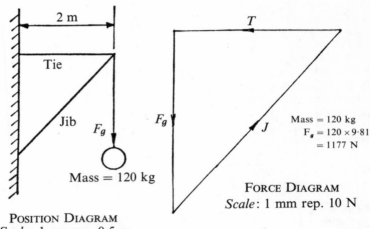

Mass = 120 kg
$F_g = 120 \times 9.81$
= 1177 N

FORCE DIAGRAM
Scale: 1 mm rep. 10 N

POSITION DIAGRAM
Scale: 1 cm rep. 0·5 m

FIG. 14

Force in the jib = 1575 N
Force in the tie = 1046 N

The Inclined Plane (Graphically)

If we examine a body resting on a smooth inclined plane (Fig. 15), we find we have an example of a three-force system for which we can draw a triangle of forces.

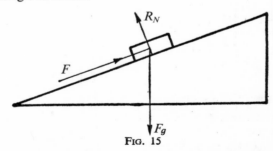

FIG. 15

When we say the plane is perfectly smooth we mean that there is no friction between the plane and the body, in this case a wooden block, so that the block will slide down the plane unless held by some force F.

Further, if the plane is smooth, the reaction R of the plane on the block will be at right angles to the plane. If there is no friction at a surface, the reaction of the surface is always at right angles to the surface. This is called the normal reaction (R_N).

The third force acting on the body is the force of gravity (F_g), i.e. its weight. We may consider the weight of the body as one force concentrated at one point in the body. This point is known as the centre of gravity and you will study it in more detail later. For the moment we will take it as being the central point of the body.

If the body is at rest on the plane, these three forces must be concurrent since they are not parallel.

We will consider two cases.

1. When the holding force is parallel to the plane

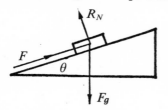 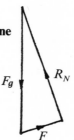

POSITION DIAGRAM

FORCE DIAGRAM

FIG. 16

If we know the angle of slope we may draw the position diagram and if we know the mass of the body we can calculate the weight F_g and draw the triangle of forces. From this we can find force F and the reaction R_N (Fig. 16).

2. When the holding force is horizontal

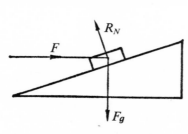

POSITION DIAGRAM

FORCE DIAGRAM

FIG. 17

Again, knowing the angle of slope, we can draw the position diagram and, using the weight of the body, we can draw the triangle of forces to find force F and the reaction R_N (Fig. 17).

These are the two most common cases, but if the holding force is acting at any other angle we can treat the problem in exactly the same way.

Example 1.

If a block of mass 90 kg rests on a smooth plane inclined to the horizontal at an angle of 20°, find the force required to support the body if it acts parallel to the plane.

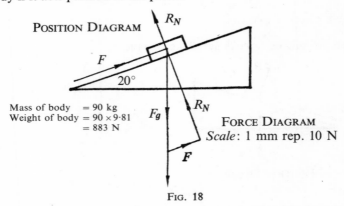

FIG. 18

Draw the block resting on a plane inclined at an angle of 20° to the horizontal (Fig. 18). It is often convenient to draw the triangle of forces directly on the weight line, so choose a suitable scale and mark off the weight to scale. Draw F parallel to the supporting force and R_N parallel to the reaction. Measure F to scale.

The force, parallel to the plane, required to support the body $= 302\ N$.

A Ladder Resting against a Wall

Another common type of problem we often meet is that of a ladder, or a beam, plank, etc., leaning against a wall.

Once again we assume the weight of the ladder to act at its centre of gravity, i.e. at the centre of the ladder. We also remember that the reaction of a smooth surface is at right angles to the surface, and that in order to achieve equilibrium the three forces must be either parallel or concurrent.

(1) If both the wall and the ground are smooth

The reaction of the wall R_1, the reaction of the ground R_2, and the weight F_g can never be concurrent. Therefore the ladder can never be in equilibrium (Fig. 19).

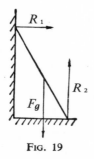 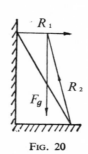 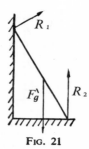

FIG. 19   FIG. 20   FIG. 21

(2) If the wall is smooth and the ground is rough

If the ground is rough the reaction at the ground will not be vertical. In this case the forces can be concurrent (Fig. 20) so that equilibrium can be obtained.

(3) If the ground is smooth and the wall is rough

No matter which way R_1 acts the forces can never be concurrent or parallel so that the ladder can never be in equilibrium (Fig. 21).

N.B.—If the top of the ladder is **fixed** to the wall the reaction at the fixing can be vertically upwards so that the forces will be parallel and the ladder can be in equilibrium.

These investigations show that a ladder resting against a wall can never be in equilibrium if the ground is smooth.

Example 1

A man of mass 90 kg stands at the middle of a ladder leaning against a smooth vertical wall. If the ladder is 4 m long and the bottom is 1·5 m from the bottom of the wall, find the reaction at the ground. (Neglect the mass of the ladder.)

We can calculate the weight of the man and we know that the reaction at the wall is horizontal (Fig. 22). These two forces meet at *P*. In order to achieve equilibrium the reaction of the ground must also pass through this point.

We can draw the triangle of forces for the three forces acting at P and so find the reactions at the wall and at the ground.

Mass of man   = 90 kg
Weight of man = 90 × 9·81 = 883 N

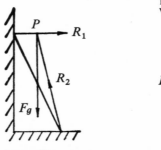

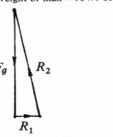

POSITION DIAGRAM
Scale: 1 cm rep. 0·5 m

FORCE DIAGRAM
Scale: 1 mm rep. 10 N

FIG. 22

Reaction at the ground = **900 N**
Reaction at wall = **180 N**

THE PARALLELOGRAM OF FORCES

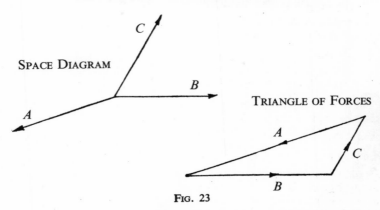

SPACE DIAGRAM

TRIANGLE OF FORCES

FIG. 23

Figure 23 shows the space diagram and triangle of forces for three forces acting at a point in equilibrium. Since each force is the equilibrant of the other two, force A is the equilibrant of forces B and C. Thus if the direction of force A in the triangle is reversed it represents the resultant R of forces B and C (Fig. 24). If we complete the parallelogram *WXYZ* on sides *B* and *C*, *WZ* may be taken to represent force *C* since *WZ* is equal to and parallel to *XY*. Thus we have a parallelogram drawn on forces *B* and *C* with *R* as a diagonal.

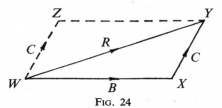

FIG. 24

From this it is seen that **if two forces acting at a point are represented in magnitude and direction by the adjacent sides of a parallelogram, then their resultant is represented in magnitude and direction by the diagonal of the parallelogram drawn from the common point.**

This theorem is known as the "parallelogram of forces" and we can verify it by experiment.

Experiment 2

Object: To verify the parallelogram of forces.

Apparatus: A drawing-board fixed vertically to the wall, a sheet of drawing-paper, two free-running pulleys, string, a supply of masses, set square and rule.

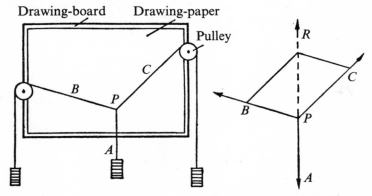

PARALLELOGRAM OF FORCES

FIG. 25

Procedure: Pin a sheet of drawing-paper to the board and fasten two pulleys at the edges of the board as shown (Fig. 25). Tie three pieces of string at a common point, tie a mass to each of the three ends, hang two of the strings over the pulleys and allow the system to come to rest taking care that the masses do not rub on the sides of the board. If the system does not come to rest with the point *P* on the paper, adjust the sizes of the masses or the position of the pulleys until it does.

Mark the position of point *P* on the paper. Calculate the magnitudes and mark the lines of action of forces *A*, *B*, and *C*. Remove the masses and pulleys and take the paper from the board.

The diagram on the paper shows the magnitude and direction of the three forces acting at the point.

Produce the line of action of force *A* backwards to give line *PR*. Choose a suitable scale and measure force *B* to scale along *PB*. Measure force *C* to the same scale along *PC*.

Using a rule and set square draw *BR* parallel to *PC* and *CR* parallel to *PB*. They should meet at point *R* on *PR*.

Measure *PR*. Length *PR* should represent a force equal in magnitude to force *A*, and if the direction of this force is taken to be the opposite of force *A*, then this force will be the resultant of forces *B* and *C* since *A* is the equilibrant of these forces.

Construct a parallelogram of forces on *A* and *B*—the diagonal should represent a force equal and opposite to force *C*.

Construct a parallelogram of forces on *A* and *C*—the diagonal should represent a force equal and opposite to force *B*.

Conclusion

When a parallelogram is constructed on any two of the forces, the diagonal of the parallelogram drawn from the common point represents their resultant in magnitude and direction.

Example 1

Two forces act at 45° to each other. If the forces are 4 N and 6 N in magnitude, find the magnitude and direction of their resultant.

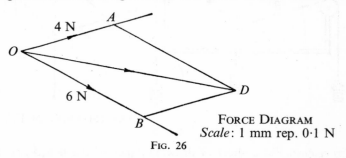

FORCE DIAGRAM
Scale: 1 mm rep. 0·1 N

FIG. 26

Draw *OA* (Fig. 26) representing a force of 4 N to scale and *OB* representing a force of 6 N to scale acting at an angle of 45° to each other.

Using a rule and set square draw *BD* parallel to *OA* and *AD* parallel to *OB* thus completing the parallelogram on *OA* and *OB*.

Measure the length of the diagonal *OD* and, using a protractor, measure angle *DOB*.

Line *OD* represents the resultant, a force of 9·3 N acting at an angle of 18½° to the 6 N force.

Example 2

Two tugs tow a ship so that the angle between the towing hawsers is 30°. If one tug exerts a force of 3 kN and the other exerts a force of 4 kN find the magnitude of the resulting force on the ship.

Force Diagram
Scale: 1 cm rep. 1 kN

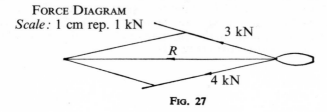

Fig. 27

Resultant force on the ship (R) = 6·8 kN

THE SIMPLE PULLEY

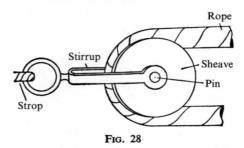

Fig. 28

Figure 28 shows a simple pulley. If there is no friction at the pin, the tension in the rope must be the same on both sides of the sheave, and if the tension in the rope is *T* N the tension in the strop must be 2*T* N.

In Fig. 29 the rope exerts two forces on the pulley, but this time the forces are inclined to the strop. Again the tension in the strop is equal

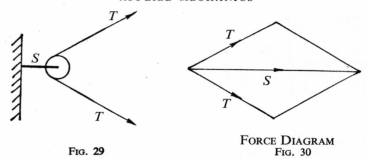

FIG. 29

FORCE DIAGRAM
FIG. 30

to the resultant of the forces exerted by the rope, but in order to find this resultant we have to draw the parallelogram of forces (Fig. 30).

As the angle between the parts of the rope is increased the tension in the strop decreases until, in the ultimate case, when the angle is 180° there is no tension in the strop (Fig. 31).

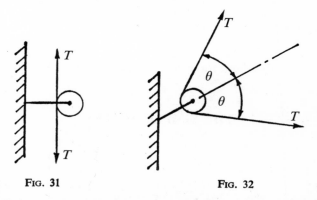

FIG. 31

FIG. 32

N.B.—If the strop is a flexible rope, the line of action of the force in the strop will always bisect the angle made by the pulley rope (Fig. 32).

Pulley problems can also be solved by using the triangle of forces for the three concurrent forces, i.e. the forces in the two parts of the rope and the tension in the strop.

The Components of a Force

Let line *AB* (Fig. 33) represent a force in magnitude and direction. If we draw a parallelogram *ADBC* on *AB* as diagonal then sides *AC* and *AD* represent two forces whose resultant is *AB*.

Clearly a whole system of forces can be drawn on *AB* to give many

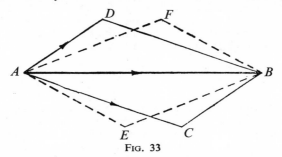

Fig. 33

pairs of forces with *AB* as the resultant of each pair, e.g. *AE* and *AF*.
In each case the two forces are known as the **components** of *AB*.

Rectangular components (graphically)

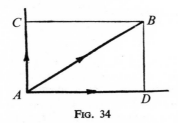

Fig. 34

We often find it very convenient to break a force into two components
at right angles to each other (Fig. 34). This is known as **resolving** the
force in two directions and the parts are known as **rectangular components, resolved parts,** or **resolutes** of the force. In this case each
resolute measures the whole effect of the given force in the direction of
the resolute.

For example, if a horse walking along a towpath is pulling a barge
along a canal, the tow rope makes an angle with the direction of motion
of the barge (Fig. 35).

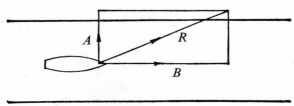

Fig. 35

The rope exerts a force R which pulls the barge along the canal but this force also tends to pull it towards the side. By drawing the parallelogram of forces, we can resolve this force into two components and find the component B which pulls the barge along the canal and the component A which pulls it towards the side.

Example 1

A loaded sledge is pulled over snow at a constant speed by a rope inclined at an angle of 30° to the ground. If the pull in the rope is 7 N, find the resistance of the ground to the motion of the sledge.

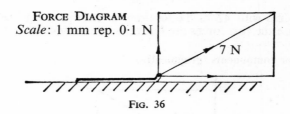

FORCE DIAGRAM
Scale: 1 mm rep. 0·1 N

7 N

FIG. 36

If we resolve the force in the rope into a horizontal and vertical component, the vertical component tends to lift the sledge, while the horizontal component pulls it over the ground.

Since the sledge moves with constant speed, the resistance of the ground is equal to the component of the force pulling the sledge.

Draw the parallelogram of forces with the 7 N force as resultant.

From the diagram, horizontal component = 6·06 N
i.e. Ground resistance = **6·06 N**

Rectangular components (analytically)

For this part of the work we require to use trigonometry. The only trigonometrical facts required are as follows:

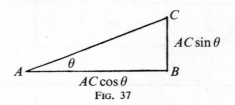

C

$AC\sin\theta$

A θ $AC\cos\theta$ B

FIG. 37

In any right-angled triangle ABC, if angle $CAB = \theta$

Sine $\theta = \dfrac{\text{opposite side}}{\text{hypotenuse}}$ Cosine $\theta = \dfrac{\text{adjacent side}}{\text{hypotenuse}}$

$\qquad\quad = \dfrac{CB}{AC}$ $\qquad\qquad\quad = \dfrac{AB}{AC}$

$\therefore$ **CB = AC sin θ** $\qquad$ $\therefore$ **AB = AC cos θ**

$$\text{Tan } \theta = \frac{CB}{AB}$$

You should also be able to look up the sine, cosine, and tangent of any angle between 0° and 90° in a book of trigonometric tables.

If force AB acts at an angle θ to the horizontal and we wish to find the horizontal and vertical components, we may draw the parallelogram of forces on AB as diagonal with component AC horizontal and component AD vertical (Fig. 38).

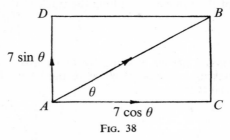

FIG. 38

If line AB is 7 units long, then line $AC = 7 \cos \theta$ units long, i.e. if line AB represents a force of 7 N then line AC will represent a force of $7 \cos \theta$ N.

Now if angle θ is 30° we find from the cosine tables that

$$\cos 30° = 0·866.$$

So that line AC represents a force of $7 \times 0·866 = 6·02$ N.

Also line $AD = $ line $BC = AB \sin \theta$.

Line AD represents a force of $7 \sin 30°$ N.

From the sine tables we find that $\sin 30° = 0·5$.

$$\therefore \text{ Force } AD = 7 \times 0·5 = 3·5 \text{ N}$$

Thus the vertical component of the force is 3·5 N and the horizontal component is 6·062 N.

This is the normal method of finding rectangular components by trigonometry. Compare this solution with the graphical solution to example 1, page 22.

Example 1

A wagon is pulled along a track by a rope inclined at an angle of 45° to the track. If the force in the rope is 500 N, find the actual force moving the wagon (Fig. 39).

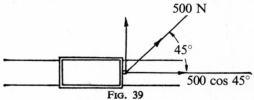

500 N

45°

500 cos 45°

Fig. 39

If we resolve the 500 N force into components, one acting along the track and the other at right angles to it, the component at right angles to the track causes no motion. Only the component of the force which acts along the track causes the wagon to move.

Component of the force acting along the track $= 500 \cos 45°$
$$= 500 \times 0.7071$$
$$= 353.5 \text{ N}$$

Example 2

A beam of mass 1200 kg is slung by two ropes, one fastened at each end and making an angle of 60° with the beam (Fig. 40). Find the tension in each rope.

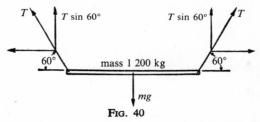

T $T \sin 60°$ $T \sin 60°$ T

60°   mass 1 200 kg   60°

mg

Fig. 40

Let the tension in each rope be T N. Since each tension has a vertical component, the two vertical components support the weight of the beam. The horizontal components balance and cancel out.

Since the tension in each rope is T N the vertical component of this tension is $T \sin 60°$

i.e. $2 \times T \sin 60° = 1\,200 \times 9.81$
$$2 \times T \times 0.866 = 1\,200 \times 9.81$$

$$T = \frac{1\,200 \times 9.81}{2 \times 0.866} = 6\,790$$

Tension in each rope $= 6\,790$ N

Finding the force when the components are known

If we know the horizontal and vertical components of the force it is a simple matter to find the force.

For example, if the horizontal component of a force is 8 N and the vertical component is 12 N, find the magnitude and direction of the force.

We can find the magnitude of the force by using the theorem of Pythagoras (Fig. 41).

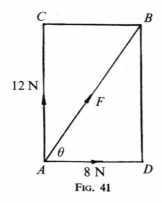

FIG. 41

$$AB^2 = AD^2 + DB^2$$

$$\text{i.e. } AB = \sqrt{AD^2 + DB^2}$$

$$= \sqrt{64 + 144}$$

$$= \sqrt{208} = \mathbf{14{\cdot}4 \ N}$$

To find the direction of force F we use the tangent of the angle θ.

$$\text{Tan } \theta = \frac{DB}{AD} = \frac{12}{8} = 1{\cdot}5$$

$$\text{Angle } \theta = 56° \ 19' \text{ (from tables)}$$

The force is of magnitude 14·4 N acting at an angle of 56° 19′ to the horizontal.

Example 1

The engine of a boat develops a thrust of 200 N to propel it through the water. If the boat is caught in a cross-current which exerts a force

of 60 N on it, find the magnitude of the resultant force on the boat and the alteration in its course (Fig. 42).

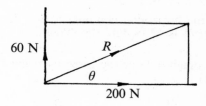

N.T.S.

Fɪɢ. 42

Resultant force on the boat $= \sqrt{200^2 + 60^2}$

$$= \sqrt{40\ 000 + 3\ 600}$$

$$= \sqrt{43\ 600}$$

$$= 208 \cdot 8$$

$$\text{Tan } \theta = \frac{60}{200}$$

$$= 0 \cdot 3$$

$$\theta = 16° 42' \text{ (from tables)}$$

Therefore the boat sails 16° 42′ off course.

The Inclined Plane (Analytically)

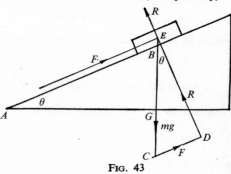

Fɪɢ. 43

Figure 43 shows a body of mass m kg held in equilibrium on a smooth inclined plane by a force F newtons acting parallel to the plane.

In triangles ABG and ECD, since CD is parallel to AB,

$$\angle ABC = \angle ECD \text{ (alternate angles)}$$

$$\angle BGA = \angle EDC \text{ (right angles)}$$

$$\therefore \angle DEC = \angle GAB = \theta$$

$$\angle DEC = \theta$$

In triangle ECD,

$$F = CD = mg \sin \theta$$

i.e. the force F required to hold the body at rest $= mg \sin \theta$ N

$$\text{also } R = DE = mg \cos \theta$$

i.e. the reaction R between the body and the plane $= mg \cos \theta$ N

If the holding force F acts horizontally as shown in (Fig. 44) only the component of F parallel to the plane prevents the body from sliding down, so that:—

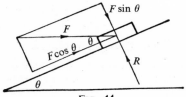

FIG. 44

$$F \cos \theta = mg \sin \theta$$

$$\text{i.e. } F = mg \tan \theta$$

The component of F perpendicular to the plane increases the reaction between the body and the plane so that

$$R = mg \cos \theta + F \sin \theta$$

When the plane is smooth the increased reaction has no effect on the holding force required, but in practical problems involving friction the increased reaction helps to prevent the body slipping down the plane. We will deal with this case more fully when studying friction.

Example

A body of mass 16 kg is held on a smooth plane inclined at an angle of 40° to the horizontal. If the holding force acts parallel to the plane, find the magnitude of the force, and the reaction between the body and the plane (Fig. 45).

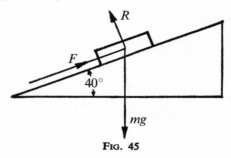

FIG. 45

Holding force $F = mg \sin \theta$
$$= 16 \times 9\cdot81 \sin 40°$$
$$= 16 \times 9\cdot81 \times 0\cdot6428$$
$$= \mathbf{100\cdot8 \ N}$$
Reaction $R = mg \cos \theta$
$$= 16 \times 9\cdot81 \times \cos 40°$$
$$= 16 \times 9\cdot81 \times 0\cdot7660$$
$$= \mathbf{120 \ N}$$

The Polygon of Forces

We have seen how we can deal with three coplanar forces acting at a point in equilibrium by using the triangle of forces.

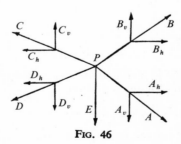

FIG. 46

Now let us consider what would happen if more than three coplanar forces acted at a point in equilibrium.

Let the point P be in equilibrium under the action of five forces A, B, C, D, and E (Fig. 46). Each of these forces can be resolved into a horizontal and vertical component which will be denoted by the suffices h and v.

If the point is in equilibrium, the vertical components acting upwards, C_v and B_v must balance the vertical components acting downwards D_v, A_v and force E.

If we draw the vectors for these forces, the total upward vector balances the total downward vector. Similarly the components acting to the right must balance the components acting to the left, i.e. B_h and A_h must balance C_h and D_h and their total vectors must be equal (Fig. 47).

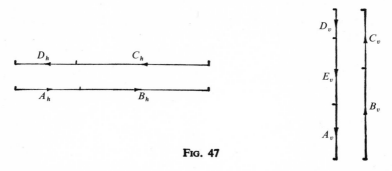

FIG. 47

Now if we combine the horizontal and vertical components in one diagram we get the following figure (Fig. 48) if the force vectors are taken successively.

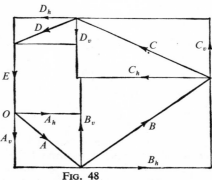

FIG. 48

If we start at a point O and draw the force vectors one after the other, since the horizontal components to the right must balance the horizontal components to the left, and the upward vertical components must balance the downward vertical components, the vectors must form a closed polygon finishing back at O.

Thus if a system of several coplanar forces is in equilibrium the forces can be represented in magnitude and direction by the sides of a closed polygon taken in order.

This theorem is known as the "polygon of forces" and before we use it we will have to devise an experiment to see if it works in practice.

Experiment 3

Object: To verify the polygon of forces.

Apparatus: We require a drawing-board mounted vertically, a sheet of drawing-paper, drawing pins, string, four pulleys, and a supply of masses.

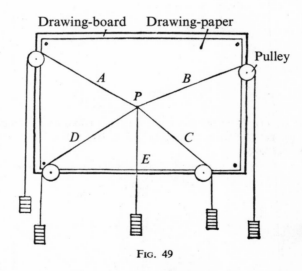

Fig. 49

Procedure: Tie several lengths of string together at a common point P and attach a mass to each free end of the string. Pin a sheet of drawing-paper to the board and fix the required number of pulleys at the edges of the board. Pass the strings over the pulleys as shown (Fig. 49) and allow the system to come to rest with the point P on the paper. If the point P does not come to rest on the paper, adjust the size of the masses until it does.

Mark the position of point P, calculate the magnitude and mark the direction of each force. Remove the masses, pulleys, and the paper from the board.

The position of point P together with the magnitudes and directions of the forces gives the space diagram of the system.

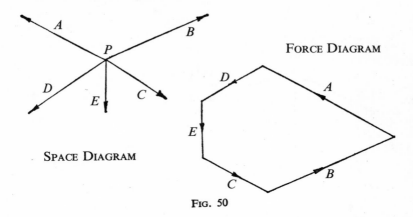

FIG. 50

Using a rule and set square choose a suitable scale and draw the vectors of the forces successively in the correct magnitude and direction (Fig. 50).

The vectors should form a closed polygon.

Notes on the polygon of forces

(1) In the statement of the theorem, the words "taken in order" refer only to the polygon and mean that each vector follows from the point where the previous one stopped. The direction arrows must also follow in order round the polygon.

The forces may be transferred from the space or structure diagram to the force diagram in any sequence since this will not affect the sums of the horizontal and the vertical components and a closed polygon will still result. If the forces are transferred from the position diagram to the force diagram in a different sequence the polygon will have a different shape, but the vectors will still form a closed polygon.

For example, if five coplanar forces in equilibrium act at point P as shown in Fig. 51 we may draw many polygons of forces, three of which are shown.

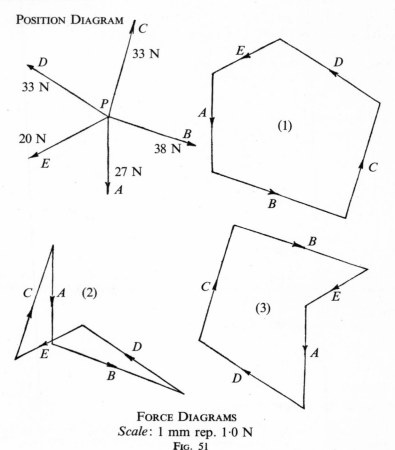

FORCE DIAGRAMS
Scale: 1 mm rep. 1·0 N
FIG. 51

In force diagram (2) the polygon crosses back on itself. This does not affect the forces or the result, and such a diagram is known as a reciprocal diagram.

Although it is not necessary to transfer the forces from the position diagram to the force diagram in any strict sequence it is advisable to adopt a definite method and work round the position diagram in a clockwise or anti-clockwise direction, taking each force in its turn. This is recommended for two reasons (i) by working to a definite method, forces are less likely to be accidentally omitted and (ii) it allows the use of Bow's notation (see later) to name the forces.

(2) When several forces act on a rigid body instead of at a point, the same conditions apply. If the body is in equilibrium, the upward vertical components of the external forces must balance the downward vertical components and the horizontal components to the right must balance the horizontal components to the left. If we draw a force diagram for the external forces acting on the body, the force vectors will form a closed polygon.

The converse of the theorem is not necessarily true when applied to a rigid body, i.e. the vector diagram may form a closed polygon although the body is not in quilibrium.

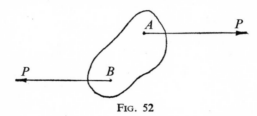

Fig. 52

For example, Fig. 52 shows a rigid body under the action of a force system. One force of the system may be *P* acting at *A* and the resultant of all the others be an equal and opposite parallel force acting at *B*. In this case the body has no tendency to move in any particular direction, but tends to rotate and is therefore not in quilibrium although the force diagram will form a closed polygon.

This situation arises when the body is acted on by a couple (see p. 57).

Example

Find the equilibrant of the forces acting on the bar shown in Fig. 53.

We can draw the polygon of forces starting at point *O* with force vectors *a. b,* and *c,* all acting downwards to give the total downward vector. The vector of the equilibrant must close the polygon, i.e. it must start at the end of vector *c* and close the polygon to the beginning of vector *a* at *O*.

The force diagram will therefore give us the magnitude and direction of the equilibrant, but it will not tell us where it acts on the body.

If it is applied along the correct straight line on the body, the external forces will balance and the body will be in equilibrium, but if it is applied in any other position, the body will rotate since it will be under the action of a couple.

This shows that the polygon of forces may be used to find the magnitude and direction of the equilibrant of a system of forces acting on a body, but that it cannot be used to find the point of application of the equilibrant.

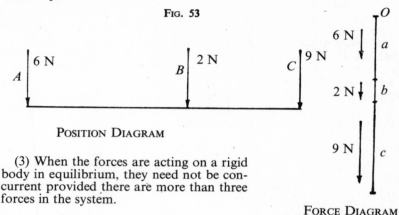

FIG. 53

POSITION DIAGRAM

FORCE DIAGRAM

(3) When the forces are acting on a rigid body in equilibrium, they need not be concurrent provided there are more than three forces in the system.

Bow's notation

This is a system of lettering forces whereby the spaces in the position or structure diagram are lettered with capital letters and each force is denoted by the letters on each side of it.

When each force is transferred to the force diagram, its vector is denoted by the two letters, but by convention small letters are used in the force diagram.

Example 1

Draw the force diagram for the concurrent force system shown in Fig. 54.

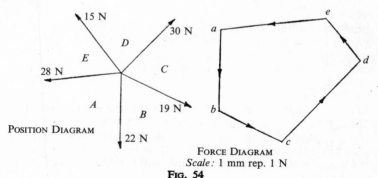

POSITION DIAGRAM

FORCE DIAGRAM
Scale: 1 mm rep. 1 N
FIG. 54

Example 2

Draw the force diagram for the system of parallel forces acting on beam *XY* in Fig. 55.

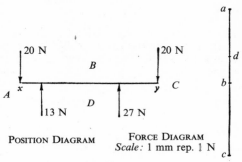

POSITION DIAGRAM   FORCE DIAGRAM
                          Scale: 1 mm rep. 1 N

FIG. 55

N.B.—When all the forces of a system are parallel the force diagram is a straight line.

Examples on the polygon of forces

Find the magnitude and direction of the equilibrant *EA* of the system of concurrent forces shown in Fig. 56.

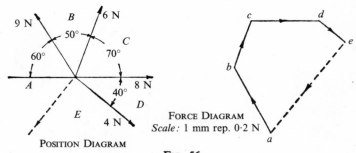

POSITION DIAGRAM   FORCE DIAGRAM
                          Scale: 1 mm rep. 0·2 N

FIG. 56

Draw the position diagram and name the forces using Bow's notation. Choose a suitable scale and draw the force diagram for the known forces. If the system is to be in equilibrium, the force diagram must be a closed polygon, therefore the vector which closes the polygon will represent the equilibrant, in magnitude and direction.

Line *ea* representing a force of 14 N acting in the direction shown is the vector of the equilibrant. Using a protractor we find that angle *dea* in the force diagram is 90°, i.e. the equilibrant *EA* acts at right angles to force *DE*.

Example 2

Figure 57 shows an iron ring fastened to a wall by an iron bolt. *AB, BC,* and *CD* are ropes pulling on the ring. If the reaction at the bolt is perpendicular to the wall, find the force *CD* and the magnitude of the reaction at the wall.

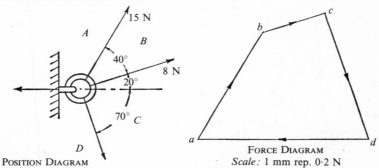

POSITION DIAGRAM

FORCE DIAGRAM
Scale: 1 mm rep. 0·2 N

FIG. 57

Choose a suitable scale and draw the force diagram for the known forces. Since we know the directions of the unknown forces we may draw their vectors, the lengths of the vectors being determined by the point where they cross.

Force *CD* = 16·8 N
Reaction at wall = 20·4 N

EXERCISES

1. A load of 60 kg is hung by two ropes as shown in Fig. 58. Find the tensions in the ropes.

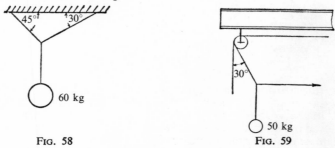

FIG. 58

FIG. 59

2. A sack of flour of mass 50 kg is hoisted to a granary on a pulley as shown in Fig. 59. Find the tensions in the hoisting rope and in the horizontal deflecting rope when the hoisting rope makes an angle of 30° with the vertical.

3. A load of 16 kg is hung from a beam by a rope. If another rope pulls the load horizontally with a force of 60 N, find the tension in the rope and the angle through which it is deflected.

4. A steel beam 5 m long has a mass of 180 kg. If it is slung from a crane hook by two 3 m ropes attached one at each end, find the tension in each rope.

5. A picture frame of mass 5 kg is held by a cord passing over a nail. If the cord makes an angle of 65° with each end of the top rail of the picture, find the tension in the cord.

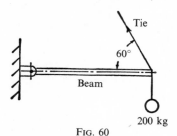

FIG. 60

6. The horizontal beam shown in Fig. 60 carries a load of 200 kg. If the tie rope makes an angle of 60° with the beam, find the forces in the beam and the tie.

7. If the jib crane shown in Fig. 61 carries a load of 600 kg, find the magnitude of the forces in the jib and the tie.

8. A load of 60 kg is suspended by two wires. If the tensions in the wires are 400 N and 550 N, find the angles which they make with the horizontal.

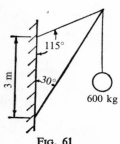

FIG. 61

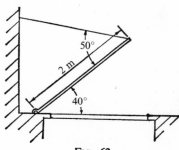

FIG. 62

9. A load of 500 kg is suspended from a horizontal beam by two wire ropes 3 m and 5 m long. If the ropes are attached to the beam at two points 5 m apart, find the tension in each rope.

10. A ladder 6 m long rests against a smooth wall and makes an angle of 50° with the ground. If a man of mass 90 kg stands at a point 3 m from the bottom of the ladder, find the magnitude and direction of the reactions at the wall and at the ground. Neglect the mass of the ladder.

11. The trap door shown in Fig. 62 is held at an angle of 40° by the cord. If the mass of the door is 250 kg, find the tension in the cord and reaction at the hinge, assuming that the total weight of the door acts at its mid-point.

12. A block of wood of mass 8 kg is placed on a smooth plane inclined at an angle of 40° to the horizontal. Find the force required to keep the block at rest
   (a) if the force acts parallel to the plane;
   (b) if the force is horizontal;
   (c) if the force acts up the plane but at an angle of 30° to the plane.

13. It requires a force of 80 N to hold a body at rest on a smooth inclined plane inclined at an angle of 25° to the horizontal. If the force acts parallel to the plane, find the mass of the body and the reaction of the plane.

14. Two forces of 5 N and 8 N act at a point. If the angle between the forces is 70°, find the magnitude and direction of the resultant force acting at the point.

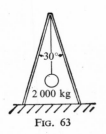

FIG. 63

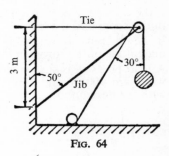

FIG. 64

15. The shear legs shown in Fig. 63 are used to lift a load of 2 000 kg. If the angle between the legs is 30°, find the force in each leg.

16. A rope running over a pulley makes an included angle of 85°. If the tension in the rope is 100 N, find the force in the pulley strop.

17. In the jib crane shown in Fig. 64, find the force in the jib and tie if the load carried is 250 kg.

18. A ship lying at anchor is acted on by the wind and the tide. If the tide exerts a pull of 460 N and the wind exerts a force of 320 N at an angle of 38° to the direction of the tide, find the resultant force in the mooring chain.

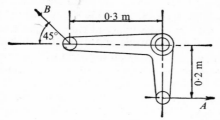

FIG. 65

19. Figure 65 shows a bell crank lever held in equilibrium by two forces A and B. If force A is 15 N, find force B and the magnitude and direction of the reaction at the pin.

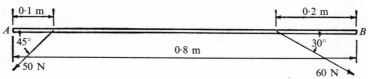

FIG. 66

20. Find the force required to balance the beam shown in Fig. 66 if the mass of the beam is 6 kg.

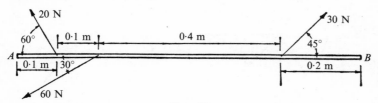

FIG. 67

21. Find the resultant of the four forces acting on the beam shown in Fig. 67, if the mass of the beam is 5 kg.

22. If a force of 24 N acts at an angle of 25° to the horizontal, find the horizontal and vertical components of the force.

23. A water skier is towed behind a boat so that the tow rope makes an angle of 45° with the direction of motion. If the tension in the rope is 400 N, calculate the resistance of the water.

24. A log is dragged by a rope which makes an angle of 32° with the ground. If the tension in the rope is 200 N, find graphically the force used to move the log forward. Check your answer by calculation.

25. A rope over a pulley makes an included angle of 62°. If the tension in the rope is 64 N, calculate the tension in the strop.

26. If two forces of 15 N and 8 N act at right angles to each other at a point, calculate the magnitude and direction of their resultant.

27. A boat crossing a river is driven forward with a force of 90 N and driven downstream by a force of 40 N. Calculate the resultant force on the boat in magnitude and direction.

28. A boy sits on a bicycle on a 25° hill. If the mass of the boy is 50 kg and the mass of the bicycle is 7 kg, calculate the force pulling him down the hill.

29. A train of pit hutches of mass 6 tonnes is held on an incline of 35°. Assuming that there is no friction, calculate the force required to hold the hutches.

    If the rope holding the hutches makes an angle of 40° with the rails and is parallel to the incline, find the tension in the rope.

30. A Vee-block is machined so that the V is an angle of 90°. If a shaft of mass 60 kg is placed in the V calculate the reactions, exerted by the sides of the block.

31. Draw the polygon of forces for the force system shown in Fig. 68.

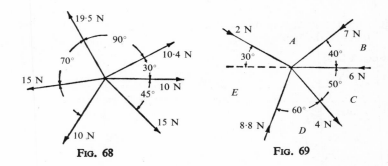

FIG. 68   FIG. 69

32. Find the magnitude and direction of the equilibrant of the forces shown in Fig. 69.

33. Four members of a frame structure meet as shown in Fig. 70. If the joint is in equilibrium, find the forces in members PQ and QS.

34. If the jib crane shown in Fig. 71 carries a load of 6 000 kg find the forces in the jib and tie.

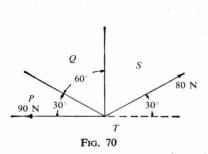

FIG. 70

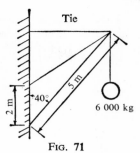

FIG. 71

35. Find the magnitude and direction of the equilibrant of the five forces acting on the light beam shown in Fig. 72. (*N.B.*—You will not be able to find the point of application of the equilibrant using the polygon of forces.)

36. Figure 73 shows a mast held in position by wire stays. Find the magnitude and direction of the reaction of the ground on the base of the mast.

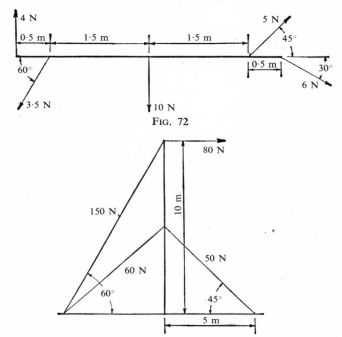

FIG. 72

FIG. 73

37. The octagon shown in Fig. 74 is acted on by the three forces shown. Find the magnitude and direction of the fourth force required to produce equilibrium. (You will not be able to find the point of application using the polygon of forces.)

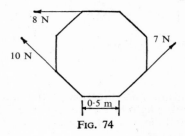

FIG. 74

MOMENTS

MOMENTS

In our earlier work a force was found to change, or tend to change, a body's state of rest or motion. Our study now leads us to investigate the effect of a force or forces acting on a body free to rotate about a fixed point or **fulcrum.** The forces themselves do not all act at the same point on the body.

Experiment 1

Object: To investigate the effect of a force acting on a body pivoted about a fixed point.

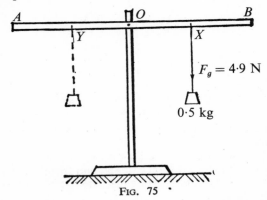

Fɪɢ. 75

Apparatus: The apparatus consists of a uniform wooden bar about 1 m long, a stand, string or cord and a selection of masses.

Procedure: The apparatus is set up so that the bar *AB* when mounted on the stand, is free to rotate about its centre *O*.

A mass of 0·5 kg is attached to a cord and suspended from any point *X* on the side *OB*. Immediately the bar rotates in a clockwise direction. If the mass is now removed from *X* to the position *Y*, the bar is made to rotate in an anti-clockwise direction. i.e. The gravitational force acting on the mass causes the bar to rotate.

Conclusion

When a force acts on a body free to rotate about a fixed point, it tends to turn the body.

This turning effect of the force is termed the **moment** of the force about the pivot or fulcrum.

In this case the 4·9 N force has a moment about point **O**.

When the force tends to produce a clockwise rotation we get a clockwise moment and when the force tends to produce an anti-clockwise rotation we get an anti-clockwise moment.

Experiment 1a

Object: To investigate the turning effect of a force.

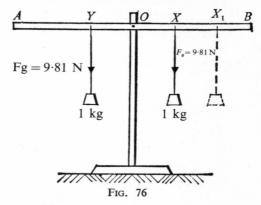

Fig. 76

Apparatus: A uniform wooden bar, a stand, string or cord and a series of masses.

Procedure: Attach a cord to a 1 kg mass and suspend it at a point Y on the side OA and at a distance of 150 mm from O. We know that the weight of this single mass will cause the bar to rotate in an anti-clockwise direction.

Another 1 kg mass is suspended at a point X on the side OB, and the distance OX adjusted so that the bar remains at rest in a horizontal position.

If the distance OX is measured, it will be found to be the same as distance OY—i.e. 150 mm.

Now replace the 1 kg mass at X by a 0·5 kg mass. The bar again rotates in an anti-clockwise direction. If the cord supporting the 0·5 kg mass is detached and the distance OX_1 readjusted so that the bar remains horizontal, it will be found to be twice that of OY.

We have now found that a force of 4·9 N can balance a force of 9·81 N if it is acting at twice the distance from the fulcrum or turning point.

If the bar is large enough, it can be shown that the 9·81 N force at *Y* can be balanced by a force of 2·45 N when *OX* is equal to 600 mm or by a force of 1·225 N when *OX* is equal to 1 200 mm and so on.

N.B.—You will notice that the product of the force and its distance from the fulcrum is equal to 1 470 units in each case, and this is balanced by the 9·81 N force at *Y*. If we take the product of the force at *Y* and its distance from the fulcrum it is also equal to 1 470 units.

Conclusions

1. The moment of a force depends on the magnitude of the force.

2. The moment also depends on the distance of the line of action of the force from the fulcrum.

Measurement of a moment

In the last experiment we saw that a small force acting some distance from the fulcrum could balance a larger force acting nearer the fulcrum. Although the forces were not equal, they had an equal turning effect about the fulcrum.

We saw further that, when the bar balanced, the product of the force on one side of the fulcrum and its distance from the fulcrum was equal to the product of the force on the other side of the fulcrum and its distance from the fulcrum.

This shows how we measure the *turning effect* or the *moment of a force*.

Moment of a force = force × distance from the fulcrum

When the force is measured in newtons and the distance is measured in metres, the moment is found in newton metre units, and written Nm.

Example

Calculate the following moments:—

Distance	Force	force × distance = Moment
1. 2 m	40 N	40 × 2 = 80 Nm
2. 150 mm	16 N	16 × 0·15 = 2·4 Nm
3. 5·4 m	25 N	25 × 5·4 = 135 Nm

Experiment 2

Object: To show that a moment is measured by the product of the force and the **perpendicular** distance from the fulcrum to the line of action of the force.

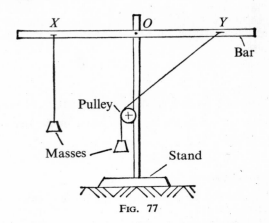

FIG. 77

Apparatus: The apparatus consists of a light bar, a stand, a free-running pulley, cord, and two equal masses.

Procedure: The light bar is fixed to the stand so that it is free to rotate about its centre O. Two masses of equal magnitude are suspended at points X and Y equidistant from O.

As in the last experiment, the bar remains horizontal under these conditions.

Now if the cord supporting one of the masses is directed over the pulley thus altering the direction of the line of action of its weight, we find the bar no longer remains at rest but rotates in the direction of the unaltered force.

Note—The pulley only serves to alter the direction of the cord. The tension in the cord in unaffected.

It would appear then, that the balance of the bar is destroyed by the alteration to the direction of the line of action of one of the forces.

A closer study of the sketch will show that only part of the original force at Y is tending to rotate the bar and part to push it to the left, i.e. the turning effect is only caused by the vertical component.

Consider the force F acting at a distance X from the turning point O (Fig. 78). Only the vertical component of F produces a turning effect, since the horizontal component passes through O, when applied at the end of the bar.

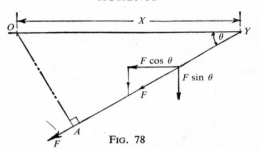

Fig. 78

$$\text{Moment} = X \times \text{vertical component of } F$$
$$= X \times F \sin \theta$$
$$= XF \sin \theta$$

But perpendicular distance OA is equal to $X \sin \theta$.
$$\text{Moment} = F \times X \sin \theta$$
$$= FX \sin \theta$$

When the bar is horizontal, the moment of the force can be found by taking either the distance as given and the vertical component of the oblique force or by taking the force as given and the perpendicular distance from the line of action of the force to the turning point.

This latter is the more usual procedure, because if the bar itself is inclined the component angle may be rather obscure.

To avoid the use of trigonometrical ratios, the following graphical method for finding the perpendicular distance may be used.

Draw the beam and load positions to scale and all the lines of action of the forces to the correct angles. The perpendicular distance from the fulcrum to the line of action of each inclined force, i.e. the turning point, may then be measured and converted back to the actual distance.

Example
Perpendicular distance
$$= FA$$
$$FA = 55 \text{ mm}$$
$$\equiv (10 \times 550 \text{ mm})$$
$$= \mathbf{550 \ mm}$$
$$= 0.55 \text{ m}$$

Take moments about F
clockwise
$$\text{moment} = (300 \times FA)$$
$$= (300 \times 0.55)$$
$$= \mathbf{165 \ Nm}$$

640 mm

Scale: 1 mm rep. 10 mm (1:10)
Fig. 79

Moments of several forces

So far we have only considered two forces acting on a body—one on either side of the fulcrum. Now we will study the effect of a number of forces of varying magnitude.

Experiment 3

Object: To study the effect of a number of forces acting on a bar.

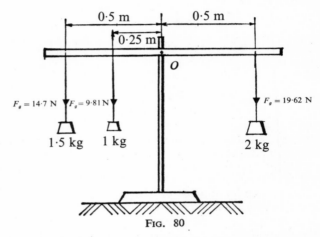

FIG. 80

Apparatus: The apparatus consists of a light bar, a stand, and masses of 2 kg, 1·5 kg and 1 kg.

Procedure: Three masses of magnitudes 1·5 kg, 1 kg and 2 kg are suspended from the bar as shown (Fig. 80).

Position the 1·5 kg and 1 kg masses 0·5 m and 0·25 m respectively to the left of the centre *O* and the 2 kg mass to the right of *O*. The position of this mass is adjusted until the bar remains at rest in a horizontal position. (It is found to be 0·5 m from *O*.)

Since the sum of the forces on the left-hand side of the bar is 24·52 N and that on the right-hand side only 10·62 N, it cannot be the magnitude of the forces alone that is producing equilibrium.

Now consider the moment of each of the forces about *O* in turn.

14·71 N.........moment $= (14·71 \times 0·5)$ Nm $= 7·35$ Nm

9·81 N.........moment $=$ $(9·81 \times 0·25)$ Nm $= 2·45$ Nm

19·62 N.........moment $= (19·62 \times 0·5)$ Nm $= 9·81$ Nm

The weight of the 1·5 kg mass and the weight of the 1 kg mass are producing anti-clockwise moments while the weight of the 2 kg mass is maintaining equilibrium by producing a clockwise turning moment.

Further study of the results show that the **sum** of the clockwise moments = the **sum** of the anti-clockwise moments.

We have the condition, then, of a bar or "body" in equilibrium while under the action of several forces.

This condition is governed by the Principle of Moments which states that:—

If a number of coplanar forces act on a body and produce equilibrium, then the sum of the clockwise moments taken about any point in the plane is equal to the sum of the anti-clockwise moments taken about the same point.

Example 1

The handle of a brake mechanism is shown in Fig. 81. If a force of 120 N is required on the brake rod R, what force must be applied to the hand grip H?

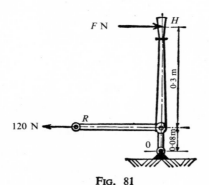

Fig. 81

Let the force at the hand grip $= F$ N

Take moments about O

By the Principle of Moments,

$$(F \times 0·38) = (120 \times 0·08)$$
$$0·38\ F = 9·6$$
$$F = 25·26 \text{ N}$$

The force required at the hand grip $= 25·26$ N

It is not always possible to neglect the weight of the body on which the forces are acting, but if the body is of uniform section and density over its length, we may assume that the whole weight of the body acts at its mid-point.

To save time and for the sake of clarity, it is usual only to draw the line joining the points of application of the forces to the fulcrum and not the full detail of the mechanism.

Example 2

A uniform beam 6 m long is pivoted at the point O and loaded as shown (Fig. 82). If the beam weighs 400 N, find the position of the 8N force from the fulcrum. Assume that the total weight of the beam acts at its centre.

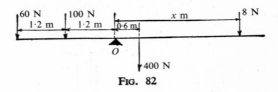

FIG. 82

Let the position of the 8 N force be X m from O.

Take moments about O

By the Principle of Moments,

$$(400 \times 0{\cdot}6) + (8 \times X) = (100 \times 1{\cdot}2) + (60 \times 2{\cdot}4)$$

$$240 + 8X = 120 + 144$$

$$8X = 264 - 240$$

$$X = \frac{24}{8}$$

$$X = 3 \text{ m}$$

Distance of the 8 N force from $O = 3$ m

Calculate, finding the distances graphically, the value of the force x which will keep the bar in equilibrium (Fig. 83).

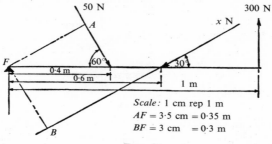

FIG. 83

Take moments about F

$$(50 \times AF) + (x \times BF) = 300 \times 1$$
$$(50 \times 0\cdot35) + (x \times 0\cdot3) = 300$$
$$0\cdot3x = 300 - 17\cdot5$$
$$= 282\cdot5$$
$$x = \mathbf{941\cdot67\ N}$$

Check:

$$(50 \times 0\cdot4 \sin 60°) + (x \times 0\cdot6 \sin 30°) = 300 \times 1$$
$$(50 \times 0\cdot3464) + (x \times 0\cdot3) = 300$$
$$17\cdot32 + 0\cdot3x = 300$$
$$0\cdot3x = 282\cdot68$$
$$x = \mathbf{942\cdot1\ N}$$
$$\text{Error} = (942\cdot1 - 941\cdot67)$$
$$= \mathbf{0\cdot43\ N}$$

(which is negligible in this case)

Levers

Any rigid bar which is free to rotate about a fixed point of support is called a lever.

Common examples are the crowbar, garden spade, wheelbarrow, rowing boat oar, safety valve, etc. To simplify the sketches of lever applications, it is usual to treat them in line or skeleton form.

The wheelbarrow, when treated in this manner, will appear as follows:

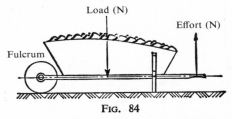

FIG. 84

In everyday conversation the term load is often taken to mean mass. In engineering, however, we are concerned with the gravitational pull on the mass and so we are inclined to talk of load in terms of force.

It must always be clear which we are using:—

e.g. a load of mass x kg, or

a load of $(x \times 9.81)$ N.

On page 53 some of the previous examples are shown in pictorial form and the appropriate lever action used in each case shown as a line diagram (Fig. 85).

From these examples it is noticed that we have varied the position of the fulcrum with respect to the load and the effort. These three variations form the basis of all lever systems.

It will also be realised that the solution of lever problems is based on the Principle of Moments.

Example 1

A crowbar is used to raise the corner of a crate. The following details are known: effective load on crowbar, 600 N; distance of corner of crate to fulcrum, 80 mm; distance from fulcrum to effort, 1 200 mm.

Calculate the effort F necessary to raise the crate (Fig. 86).

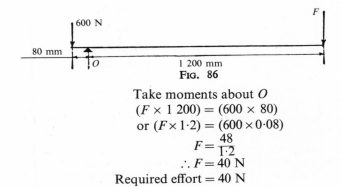

FIG. 86

Take moments about O

$$(F \times 1\ 200) = (600 \times 80)$$

or $(F \times 1.2) = (600 \times 0.08)$

$$F = \frac{48}{1.2}$$

$$\therefore F = 40 \text{ N}$$

Required effort $= 40$ N

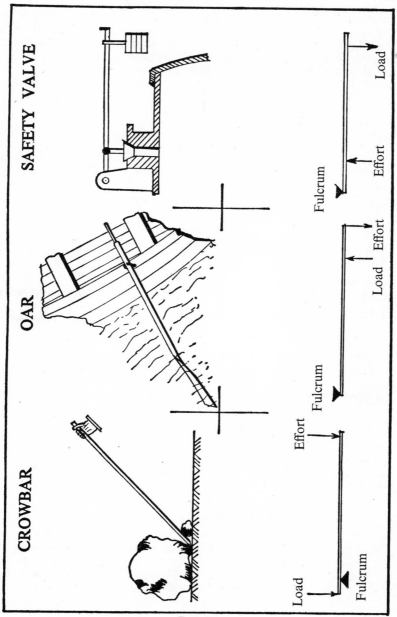

FIG. 85

Example 2

The resultant load on a wheelbarrow is estimated at 448 N. If it is assumed to act at a distance of 0·46 m from the fulcrum (the axle) and the effort necessary on the shafts to balance the load is 224 N, calculate the length of the shafts (Fig. 87).

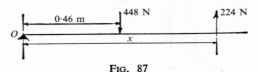

FIG. 87

Take moments about O
$$448 \times 0.46 = X \times 224$$
$$\therefore X = \frac{448 \times 0.46}{224}$$
$$= 0.92 \text{ m}$$

The length of the shafts (from the axle) is 0·92 m.

Example 3

During the testing of a "Lever Safety Valve" (Fig. 88) the following data was recorded:—

Boiler pressure	$1\ 034 \times 10^3$ N/m^2
Area of valve	$0.001\ 3$ m^2
Distance from valve to fulcrum	0.076 m
Distance from fulcrum to counter balance	0.38 m

Calculate the mass of the counter balance.

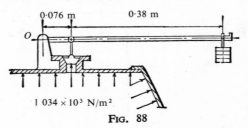

FIG. 88

Note—Before attempting this problem we must realise that the pressure in the boiler means that for every square metre of the boiler surface there is a thrust of $1\ 034 \times 10^3$ N. Since the valve has an area of 0·001 3 m^2, the total thrust on it must be ($1\ 034 \times 10^3 \times 0.001\ 3$) N.

Take moments about O
Let gravitational force on counterbalance be F_g N

$$(F_g \times 0.456) = (1\,034 \times 10^3 \times 0.001\,3) \times 0.076$$
$$0.456\,F_g = 102.16$$
$$F_g = 224 \text{ N}$$

$\therefore$ Mass of counterbalance $= \dfrac{224}{9.81}$ kg $= 22.86$ kg.

Bell crank lever

When the direction of a force has to be altered, the lever may be bent to the appropriate angle. A simple form is the bell crank (Fig. 89).

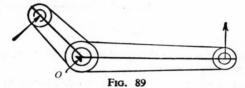

FIG. 89

The angle between the arms will depend on the angle at which the forces are required to act. Examples of the bell crank lever can be seen on a bicycle brake system (lever type), railway signal and points gear, etc.

Example 1

Calculate the force FN acting on the bell crank lever shown in Fig. 90.

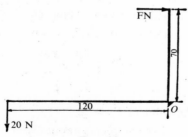

FIG. 90

Take moments about O
$$(F \times 70) = (20 \times 120)$$
$$\therefore F = \frac{20 \times 120}{70}$$
$$\therefore F = 34.28 \text{ N}.$$

Often one particular type of lever will not satisfy all the demands required in the design of the mechanism. Several forms may then be used in conjunction with each other.

Example 1

Calculate the weight F_g which can be carried by the compound lever system shown in Fig. 91.

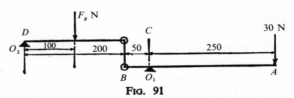

FIG. 91

Before attempting to solve this problem, it will be helpful to study the working of the arrangement.

Lever *AB* is pivoted at O_1 and the effort produces a moment about O_1 which is balanced by the moment of a force acting at *B*. This force is transmitted to lever *CD*, pivoted at O_2 by the connecting member or *link BC*.

It is the moment of this force which has to balance the moment of F_g about O_2.

Calculation

First, to find the force in the link *BC*.

$$\text{Take moments about } O_1$$

$$(30 \times 250) = (BC \times 50)$$

$$\therefore BC = \frac{30 \times 250}{50}$$

$$\therefore BC = 150 \text{ N}$$

Second, to find the value of F_g.

$$\text{Take moments about } O_2$$

$$(F_g \times 100) = (150 \times 200)$$

$$\therefore F_g = \frac{150 \times 200}{100}$$

$$= 300 \text{ N}$$

The weight which can be carried by the given system = 300 N.

Couples

If two equal and opposite forces act at
the centre of a light rod, the rod remains
in equilibrium, but if the forces are displaced an equal distance D metres from
the centre of the rod as shown (Fig. 92)

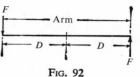

FIG. 92

they will obviously cause the rod to rotate about the centre.

(*N.B.*—There is no pivot at the centre.)

This kind of force system is known as a couple and the moment of
the couple about the centre is $2 \times F \times D$ Nm.

In calculating the moment of a couple we generally use the distance
between the forces, known as the arm of the couple so that

$$\text{the moment of the couple} = 2 \times F \times D$$
$$= \text{force} \times \text{arm of the couple.}$$

It is worth noting that a couple can be balanced only by another couple.

Reactions of Beam Supports

A reaction, we have found, is always brought into play when a force
acts on a rigid body.

Let us suppose that we have a wooden bar supported at the point F
and supporting the masses shown in Fig. 93. The sum of the weights
$(5 \times 9\cdot81 + 7\cdot5 \times 9\cdot81)$ N must be completely balanced by a force
producing an upthrust at F. This upthrust is known as a **reaction.**

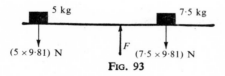

FIG. 93

Reactions for parallel force systems
Single support—one reaction

In earlier work on moments, the problems dealt with only one
support, i.e. the fulcrum.

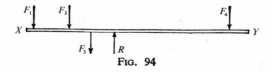

FIG. 94

C

The beam XY is in equilibrium when loaded as shown in Fig. 94. All the forces act vertically down so that the reaction in the single support must act vertically up. The magnitude of the reaction will be equal to the sum of all the forces, i.e. $F_1 + F_2 + F_3 + F_4$

Example

The beam shown in Fig. 95 carries five vertical loads and is in equilibrium. Calculate the reaction R.

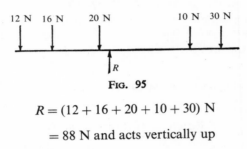

Fig. 95

$$R = (12 + 16 + 20 + 10 + 30)\ N$$

$$= 88\ N \text{ and acts vertically up}$$

Two supports

The principle of moments can also be applied to problems involving two supports, e.g. a roof truss supported on walls, bridges supported by the banks of a river or by piers, wall cranes, etc.

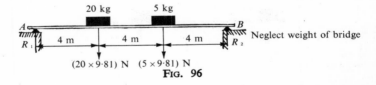

Fig. 96

In Fig. 96 we have a bridge 12 m long supported by two piers, A and B. The piers resist the given loading by the reactions at A and B, and to calculate their values we apply the Principle of Moments.

Let R_1 act at the point A and R_2 act at the point B. If we take moments about the point A, the reaction R_1 cannot have a moment as its line of action passes through the fulcrum, i.e. the perpendicular distance from the line of action to the fulcrum is zero. Thus by taking moments about one point of support we are able to calculate the value of the other.

Take moments about R_1

$$(20 \times 9\cdot81 \times 4) + (5 \times 9\cdot81 \times 8) = R_2 \times 12$$
$$9\cdot81\,(80 + 40) = 12\,R_2$$
$$\therefore R_2 = \frac{9\cdot81 \times 120}{12}$$
$$= \mathbf{98\cdot1\ N}$$

Now taking moments about R_2

$$12R_1 = (5 \times 9\cdot81 \times 4) + (20 \times 9\cdot81 \times 8)$$
$$= 9\cdot81\,(20 + 160)$$
$$\therefore R_1 = \frac{9\cdot81 \times 180}{12}$$
$$= \mathbf{147\cdot15\ N}$$

Since all the forces are acting vertically down, both reactions are acting vertically up and

the sum of the downward forces = the sum of the upward forces

$$196\cdot2 + 49\cdot05 = 147\cdot15 + 98\cdot1$$
$$245\cdot25 = 245\cdot25$$

It is seen from this that only one reaction need be calculated in a parallel force system such as this.. The other reaction may be found by subtracting the calculated reaction from the total load supported by both.

Conditions of equilibrium

In order to be in equilibrium under the action of several forces a body must not tend to move in any direction, or to rotate about an axis. This is achieved as follows:—

(1) In a two-force system

    (a) the forces must be equal in magnitude, opposite in direction and act in the same straight line.

(2) In a three-force system

    (a) the forces must be coplanar;

    (b) The lines of action of the forces must be parallel or concurrent;

    (c) the algebraic sum of the moments of the forces about any point in the plane must be zero.

(3) In a system of more than three coplanar forces

    (*a*) the algebraic sum of the horizontal components of the forces must be zero;

    (*b*) the algebraic sum of the vertical components of the forces must be zero;

    (*c*) the algebraic sum of the moments of the forces about any point in the plane must be zero.

N.B.—In a system of more than three coplanar forces acting on a rigid body, the forces need not be parallel or concurrent.

Driving torque

In the first experiment we carried out in moments, we found that if a force acted on a body pivoted at a point, then the body tended to rotate about the pivot.

When a force acts on a body and makes it turn or twist, we say that the body is subjected to a **torque**. The turning effect or moment of a force is a torque and, as before, is measured by the product of the force and the perpendicular distance from the pivot to the line of action of the force.

The unit of torque is the same as that used for the moment of a force, i.e. newton metres (Nm).

FIG. 97

FIG. 98

Example 1

The force applied to a handwheel (Fig. 97) is 60 N. If the effective radius is 0·25 m, what torque will be produced?

$$\text{Torque} = \text{force} \times \text{perpendicular distance}$$

$$= 60 \times 0\cdot25$$

$$= \mathbf{15\ Nm}$$

Example 2

Steam is directed on to the vanes of a turbine rotor at an effective radius of 0·6 m. If the resulting torque is 804 Nm, calculate the force supplied by the steam (Fig. 98).

$$\text{Torque} = \text{force} \times \text{perpendicular distance}$$
$$\text{Force} = \text{Torque} \div \text{radius}$$
$$= \frac{804}{0·6}$$
$$= \mathbf{1\ 340\ N}$$

EXERCISES

1. A light uniform bar is pivoted about its mid-point and a mass of 5 kg is hung at a distance of 580 mm from the pivot. At what distance on the other side of the pivot should a mass of 20 kg be hung so that the bar will remain at rest?

2. A uniform beam 6 m long weighs 500 N and is free to rotate about a point 2 m from one end. What force must act at this end so that the beam will remain at rest in a horizontal position?

3. Two bodies of mass 14 kg and 10 kg are suspended from points 600 mm and 750 mm respectively from the left-hand end of a uniform beam 4 m long. If the beam weighs 120 N, what mass must be suspended 300 mm from the right-hand end to keep the beam horizontal when the whole arrangement is suspended from a chain attached to the mid-point of the beam?

   What will be the tension in the chain?

4. A right-angled bell crank lever has arms 150 mm and 200 mm long. If a force of 80 N is applied at right angles to the end of the 200 mm arm, what will be the force created at the end of the 150 mm arm?

5. The uniform beam shown in Fig. 99 weighs 80 N and has to be in equilibrium when loaded as shown. Calculate the position of the single support, R.

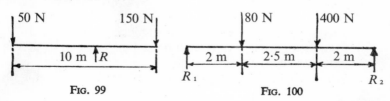

FIG. 99   FIG. 100

6. Calculate the reactions R_1 and R_2 on the uniform beam shown in Fig. 100. (Neglect the weight of the beam.)

7. Calculate the reactions R_a and R_b on the uniform beam loaded as shown in Fig. 101. The beam weighs 1000 N.

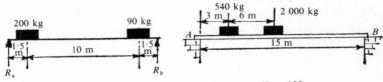

FIG. 101   FIG. 102

8. The bridge represented in Fig. 102 is subjected to estimated loads of 540 kg and 2 000 kg as shown. Determine the load on the piers A and B if the mass of the structure is 20 000 kg.

9. The diving-board shown in Fig. 103 is held in position by two supports. When in use, a force of 600 N is exerted on the free end. What force is transmitted to the supports S_1 and S_2?

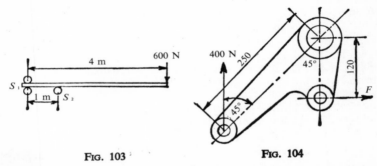

FIG. 103   FIG. 104

10. Railway points are operated from a signal cabin by a hand-operated lever. Movement of this lever operates a bell crank lever (Fig. 104). If the operating force is 400 N, find the force F actuating the points.

11. A dockside crane, shown diagrammatically in Fig. 105, is mounted on rails. If the safe working load (S.W.L.) must not exceed 2×10^3 kg

   (a) calculate the least distance of the stabilising load of 4×10^3 kg from the right-hand support at maximum S.W.L. (Neglect the weight of the structure.)

   (b) What will be the reaction at the left-hand support for this condition?

   (c) In which direction must the stabilising load be moved to increase the stability of the crane?

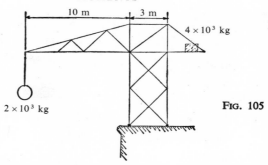

FIG. 105

12. When used for uprooting trees, a truck of mass 1 500 kg has a wire rope attached to it at a point 200 mm above the centre of the wheels. The tension in the rope is estimated to be 2 000 N and the rope remains parallel to the ground and in line with the centre line of the truck. The distance between the wheel centres is 4 m and the weight of the truck acts 1·2 m to the rear of the front axle. Calculate the reaction of all four wheels with the ground.

13. The angle of elevation of the crane jib shown in Fig. 106 can be altered by two power-operated screw ties. When the jib member *CB* makes an angle of 30° to the hirozintal, the member *AB* makes an angle of 90° with the ties.

   Calculate the tension in each tie when the load to be raised is 3×10^3 kg

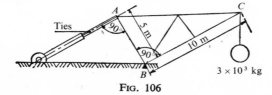

FIG. 106

14. Part of a hand-operated brake mechanism is shown in Fig. 107. Calculate the force imparted to the brake shoe when the applied force is 150 N

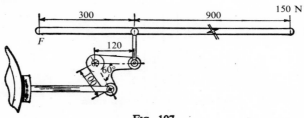

FIG. 107

15. Part of a heavy-duty weighing machine is in the form of a compound lever system (Fig. 108). What effort *P* is necessary to balance a load of 1 000 kg placed centrally on the platform?

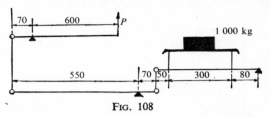

FIG. 108

16. Figure 109 shows the outline of a bicycle brake mechanism. Find the force (F) exerted on the rim of the wheel by each brake block.

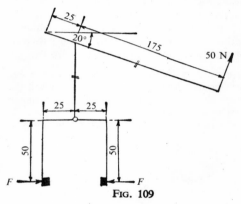

FIG. 109

17. A fence post supports three wires and is braced as shown in the sketch (Fig. 110). Calculate the tension *T* which will keep the post vertical.

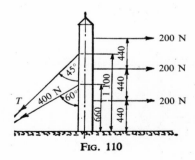

FIG. 110

18. A steel girder weighing 5×10^3 N is slung into position by two wire ropes (Fig. 111). In order that the girder may clear obstructions, it is necessary to tilt one end so that the axis of the girder makes an angle of 25° with the horizontal. Find the tensions in each rope when the left-hand rope makes $67\frac{1}{2}°$ with the horizontal and the right-hand rope is at right angles to the axis of the girder.

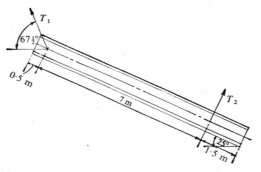

FIG. 111

CHAPTER III

CENTRE OF GRAVITY

Every concrete body (i.e. everything made of solid, liquid, or gaseous material) has mass, and, therefore, when near the surface of the Earth it is attracted to the Earth by the force of gravity. Thus it has weight.

Every small particle of the body has a weight of its own and the weight of the body acts throughout the whole body. It is often very convenient to assume that the weight of the whole body is concentrated at one point.

You will see this clearly if we examine a straight rod made of one material and having the same breadth and thickness throughout its length.

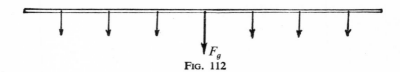

F_g

FIG. 112

Imagine the rod to be divided into many small parts. Each small piece has a weight of its own and the small individual weights form a parallel force system (Fig. 112). The magnitude of the resultant of all the small forces is equal to the weight of the rod and, by symmetry, it acts at the centre of the rod.

If the rod is laid on a knife edge it will be found that it balances when the knife edge is exactly under the centre. The reaction in the knife edge supplies the equilibrant of the force system and the equilibrant, of course, acts directly opposite to the resultant.

When dealing with the weight of the rod we may assume that the total weight is concentrated at one point at the centre of the rod. This point is known as the centre of gravity.

The centre of gravity of a body is the fixed point relative to the body through which the total weight of the body may always be considered to act.

66

Centre of gravity of a rectangular plate

If we examine a flat rectangular plate of uniform density and thickness, we see that it can be divided up into a number of strips each similar to a uniform rod (Fig. 113). The centre of gravity of each strip is at its mid point so that the centre of gravity of the whole body will lie on the line AB connecting the centres of gravity of the strips.

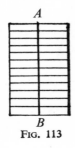

Fig. 113

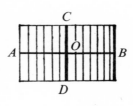

Fig. 114

If the body is now turned on its side (Fig. 114), we can repeat the procedure and we find that the centre of gravity lies on line CD.

Since the centre of gravity lies on both lines, it must be at the intersection O.

In practice this point O may be found much more easily by taking the intersection of the diagonals (Fig. 115).

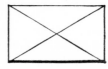

Fig. 115

Centre of gravity of a rectangle is at the point where the diagonals intersect.

Centre of area

When dealing with a thin flat plate of material of uniform density and thickness (generally called a lamina), we can find the centre of area of the geometric shape of the lamina and take that point as being the centre of gravity. This is quite permissible since the weight of the body is proportional to the area of the body if the thickness is constant.

This centre of area is often referred to as the centroid.

Centroid of a triangular lamina

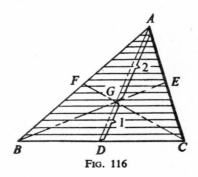

FIG. 116

The triangular lamina ABC, may be divided into a number of narrow strips parallel to side BC. Since the centre of gravity of each strip lies at its mid point, the centroid of the lamina must lie on AD—i.e. on the line joining the mid point of BC to A.

This line is known as a **median.**

By taking the strips parallel to side AC, we find that the centroid must lie on the median BE, and similarly it must also lie on the median CF. i.e. the centroid lies at G, the intersection of the medians.

The medians of any triangle intersect in

the ratio $2:1$; in this case $\dfrac{AG}{GD} = \dfrac{2}{1}$

The following sketches Fig. 117 show the position of the centre of gravity in some of the more elementary shapes.

(i)   **Rectangle**   *C. G.*—At the intersection of the diagonals.

                             Area —Length × Breadth.

(ii)   **Triangle**   *C. G.*—At the intersection of the medians.

                             Area —$\frac{1}{2}$ Base × Altitude.

(iii)   **Circle**   *C. G.*—At the centre.

                             Area —$\dfrac{\pi D^2}{4}$ or πr^2

(iv)   **Semicircle**   *C. G.*—At a distance of $\dfrac{4R}{3\pi}$ perpendicular from the centre of the diameter.

                             Area —$\dfrac{\pi D^2}{8}$ or $\dfrac{\pi r^2}{2}$

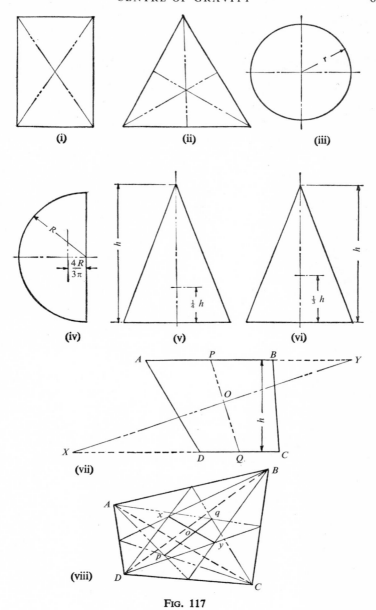

Fig. 117

(v) **Cone (solid)**   *C. G.*—$\frac{1}{4}h$ up from the base.
                 Volume—$\frac{1}{3}\pi r^2 h$

(vi) **Conical surface** *C. G.*—$\frac{1}{3}h$ up from the base.

(vii) **Trapezium**   *C. G.*—At the intersection of XY and PQ.
                                   To draw XY   Produce AB to Y such that $BY = DC$.
                                                 Produce CD to X such that $DX = BA$.
                                                        Join XY.

                                 To draw PQ P is the mid point of AB and Q is the mid point of DC.
                                                   Join PQ.

$$Area - \left(\frac{AB + CD}{2}\right)h$$

(viii) **Any quadrilateral (graphically)**   *C. G.*—(1) Join DB to give $\triangle DAB$ and $\triangle DCB$. Find the centre of gravity of each triangle and join (XY)

                                      (2) Join AC to give $\triangle ADC$ and $\triangle ABC$. Find the centre of gravity of each triangle and join (PQ)

                                    The intersection of XY and PQ gives the centre of gravity of quadrilateral $ABCD$ at O.

Centroid of an irregular lamina

We have seen that the total weight of the lamina may be considered to be concentrated at the centroid.

Imagine an irregular lamina to be suspended at a point P so that it is free to rotate about P (Fig. 118).

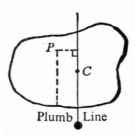

Plumb Line

FIG. 118

The total weight of the lamina is concentrated at the centroid C so that its weight supplies a turning moment which rotates the body. The moment will cease to exist and the body will remain at rest when the line of action of the weight passes through P—i.e. when the centroid is directly under the point of suspension.

We use this fact when we determine the centroid of an irregular lamina by experiment.

Experiment

Object: To find the centroid of an irregular lamina.

Apparatus: An irregular lamina, a point of suspension and a plumb line.

Procedure: Hang the body from the point of suspension and allow it to come to rest. Hang the plumb line from the same point of suspension and mark the trace of the plumb line on the lamina. The centroid of the lamina must lie on this trace, i.e. P_1A. (Fig. 119).

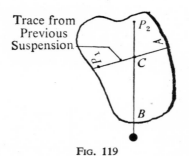

Trace from
Previous
Suspension

FIG. 119

Suspend the lamina in another position and again mark the trace of the plumb line P_2B.

The centroid of the lamina is at the point where the traces intersect.

The lamina may be suspended in several positions and in each case the trace of the plumb line will pass through the centroid.

Example 1.

AB is a uniform bar of mass 4 kg carrying metal blocks clamped on as shown, Fig. 120. Calculate the position of the centre of gravity of the arrangement.

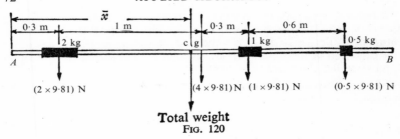

Total weight
FIG. 120

Let distance of C. G. from A be $\bar{x}$

Take moments about A

Sum of individual moments = Total moment

$(0.3 \times 2 \times 9.81) + (1.3 \times 4 \times 9.81) + (1.6 \times 1 \times 9.81) +$
$(2.2 \times 0.5 \times 9.81) \quad = (\bar{x} \times 7.5 \times 9.81)$
$9.81 (0.6 + 5.2 + 1.6 + 1.1) = 9.81 (7.5\ \bar{x})$

$$\therefore \bar{x} = \frac{8.5}{7.5}$$

$$= 1.135 \text{ m}$$

i.e. The centre of gravity of the loaded bar lies at a point 1·135 m from A.

Composite shapes

In a composite shape the whole shape is made up of two or more simple or basic shapes.

Example 1.

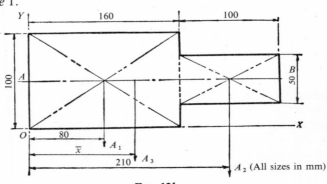

FIG. 121

Fig. 121 shows a shape which is made up of two rectangles on a common centre line or axis, *AB*. As it is also symmetrical about this axis, the centre of gravity will lie on the axis.

We also know that the total weight of each shape will act through the centre of gravity of that shape—in this case, the intersection of the diagonals.

The resultant of weight A_1 and weight A_2 will give the position of the point where the combined weight will act, i.e. the centre of gravity.

Since the weight of each part is proportional to its area, our calculation may be simplified by using area to represent weight.

$$\text{Area:} \ A_1 = (100 \times 160) \qquad \text{Area:} \ A_2 = (50 \times 100)$$
$$= 16 \times 10^3 \text{ mm}^2 \qquad\qquad = 5 \times 10^3 \text{ mm}^2$$
$$\text{Combined area:} \ A_3(16 + 5) \ 10^3$$
$$= 21 \times 10^3 \text{ mm}^2$$

The sum of the individual moments of area must equal the moment of area of the **whole** shape.

Take moments about OY   *Let $\bar{x}$ be distance of A_3 from OY*

Sum of clockwise moments = Total clockwise moment
$$(80 \times A_1) + (210 \times A_2) = (\bar{x} \times A_3)$$
$$[(80 \times 16) + (210 \times 5)] \ 10^3 = (\bar{x} \times 21) \ 10^3$$
$$1 \ 280 + 1 \ 050 = 21\bar{x}$$
$$\bar{x} = 111 \text{ mm}$$

∴ **The centre of gravity of whole shape lies 111 mm from OY axis on the centre line AB.**

Example 2.

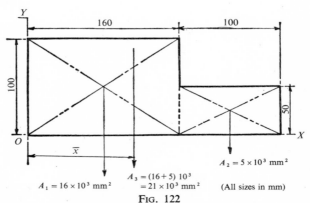

$$A_1 = 16 \times 10^3 \text{ mm}^2 \qquad A_3 = (16 + 5) \ 10^3$$
$$= 21 \times 10^3 \text{ mm}^2 \qquad \text{(All sizes in mm)}$$

$$A_2 = 5 \times 10^3 \text{ mm}^2$$

FIG. 122

The shape (Fig. 122) no longer has an axis of symmetry and the position of the centre of gravity must be calculated both up from OX axis and to the right from OY axis.

First consider the shape to be resting on the OX axis

Let the distance of C. G. from OY be $\bar{x}$

Take moments about OY

Sum of clockwise moments = Total clockwise moment

$$(80 \times A_1) \times (210\,A_2) = (\bar{x} \times A_3)$$
$$[(80 \times 16) + (210 \times 5)]10^3 = (\bar{x} \times 21)10^3$$
$$\bar{x} = \frac{2\,330}{21}$$
$$\therefore \bar{x} = \mathbf{111\ mm}$$

∴ The centre of gravity lies 111 mm from OY axis

Now consider the shape resting on the OY axis (Fig. 123).

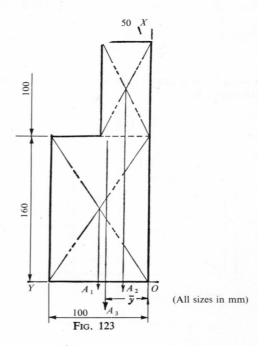

(All sizes in mm)

Fig. 123

Let the distance of C. G. from OX be $\bar{y}$

Take moments about OX

Sum of anti-clockwise moments = Total anti-clockwise moment

$$(\bar{y} \times 21)10^3 = [(25 \times 5) + (50 \times 16)]10^3$$

$$21\bar{y} = 925$$

$$\bar{y} = \frac{925}{21}$$

$$\bar{y} = \textbf{44·04 mm}$$

∴ **The centre of gravity lies 44·04 mm from OX axis.**

i.e. the centre of gravity of the whole shape lies at a point 111 mm from OY axis and 44·04 mm from OX axis.

Analysing this solution we find that the following steps were taken:—

(1) The shape as a whole was broken down into elementary shapes.

(2) The area of each shape was calculated.

(3) The distance from the reference axis to the centre of gravity of each shape was calculated.

(4) The moment of each shape about an axis was calculated.

(5) The moment of the whole body was equated to the sum of the moments of the individual parts.

All this information can be put in tabular form giving a much more compact solution.

Part	Area of each part (mm^2)	Distance of C.G. from OY axis (mm)	Moment of Area about OY axis (mm^3)	Distance of C.G. from OX axis (mm)	Moment of Area about OX axis (mm^3)
1	$160 \times 100 =$ 16×10^3	80	$16 \times 10^3 \times 80 =$ 128×10^4	50	$16 \times 10^3 \times 50 =$ 800×10^3
2	$100 \times 50 =$ 5×10^3	210	$5 \times 10^3 \times 210 =$ 105×10^4	25	$5 \times 10^3 \times 25 =$ 125×10^3

$\Sigma A = 21 \times 10^3$ $\Sigma AX = 233\,10^4$ $\Sigma AY\,925 \times 10^3$
$= 2\,330 \times 10^3$

Part:—The shape is broken into a number of basic shapes such as rectangles, triangles, circles, etc.

Area—The area of each part is calculated.

Distance—The distance of the centre of gravity of each part from the OY axis (X) and from the OX axis (Y) is taken.

ΣA—Represents the sum of the individual areas.

ΣAx and ΣAy—Represent the sums of the individual moments.

$\bar{X}$—Denotes the distance of the centre of gravity of the **whole shape** from the OY axis.

$\bar{Y}$—Similarly, this is the distance of the centre of gravity of the **whole shape** from the OX axis.

$$\Sigma A\bar{Y} = \Sigma AY \qquad\qquad \Sigma A\bar{X} = \Sigma AX$$

$$\bar{Y} = \frac{\Sigma AY}{\Sigma A} \qquad\qquad \bar{X} = \frac{\Sigma AY}{\Sigma A}$$

$$= \frac{925}{21} \qquad\qquad\quad = \frac{2\,330}{21}$$

$$= 44\cdot04 \text{ mm} \qquad\qquad = 111 \text{ mm}$$

∴ **The centre of gravity of the shape lies at a point 44·04 mm from OX axis and 111 mm from OY axis.**

Negative quantities

When considering a shape which has parts cut away, the missing portions may be treated as negative quantities.

Example

Find the centroid of the shape shown in Fig. 124.

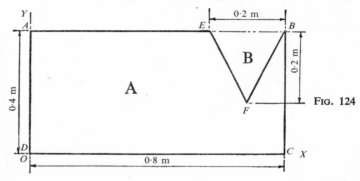

Fig. 124

The basic shape here is the rectangle $ABCD$. Triangle EFB has been cut away from one side. The remaining area will be equal to:—

Area of rectangle $ABCD$ (Part A)—Area of triangle EFB (Part B).

Part	Area (A) (m²)	X (m)	AX (m³)	Y (m²)	AY (m³)
A	$0\cdot4 \times 0\cdot8 = \quad 0\cdot32$	0·4	0·128	0·2	0·064
B	$-(0\cdot1 \times 0\cdot2) = -0\cdot02$	0·7	$-0\cdot014$	0·333	$-0\cdot007$

$$\Sigma A = 0\cdot3 \qquad \Sigma AX = 0\cdot114 \qquad \Sigma AY = 0\cdot057$$

$$\Sigma A\bar{X} = \Sigma AX \qquad\qquad \Sigma A\bar{Y} = \Sigma AY$$

$$\bar{X} = \frac{\Sigma AX}{\Sigma A} \qquad\qquad \bar{Y} = \frac{\Sigma AY}{\Sigma A}$$

$$= \frac{0\cdot114}{0\cdot3} \qquad\qquad = \frac{0\cdot057}{0\cdot3}$$

$$= 0\cdot38 \text{ m} \qquad\qquad = 0\cdot19 \text{ m}$$

i.e. **The centre of gravity of the shape lies at a point 0·38 m from OY axis and 0·19 m from OX axis.**

Centre of gravity of solids

When dealing with solid bodies—i.e. three dimensions—we may have to consider either their weights or their volumes. In both cases the calculation necessary is virtually the same as when dealing with area; the weight or volume being substituted for the area.

Column 2 in the table may now give the weight or volume of the part under consideration and the moment found will be that of weight or volume.

The position of the centre of gravity of solid bodies is located by three dimensions—on its length, on its breadth and on its height.

Example

Calculate the position of the centre of gravity of the shaped block shown in the sketch (Fig. 125). (All dimensions in mm.)

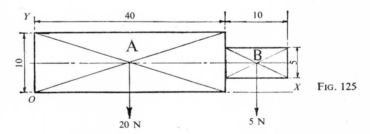

FIG. 125

Note:—Part *A*—Rectangular Prism 40 × 10 × 10

Part *B*—Rectangular Prism 10 × 5 × 5

Part	Weight (F_g N)	x (mm)	Moment $F_g\, x$
A	20	20	20 × 20 = 400
B	5	45	5 × 45 = 225
	$\Sigma F_g = 25$N		$\Sigma F_g x = 625$ Nm

$$\Sigma F_g \bar{x} = \Sigma F_g x$$
$$\bar{x} = \frac{\Sigma F_g x}{\Sigma F_g}$$
$$= \frac{625}{25}$$
$$= 25 \text{ mm}$$

i.e. The centre of gravity lies at a distance of 25 mm from OY.

Since this is a 3-dimensional body, the position of the *C. G.* is within the body at a point 25 mm from *O Y*, 5 mm up from *OX* and 5 mm from back to front.

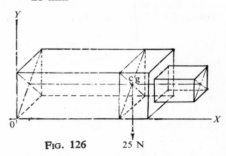

Fig. 126   25 N

Example

Calculate the position of the *C. G.* of the turned shaft shown in Fig. 127.

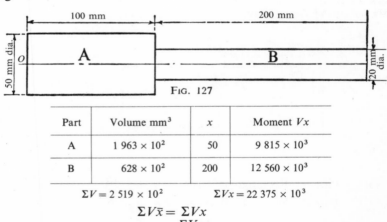

Fig. 127

Part	Volume mm^3	x	Moment Vx
A	$1\ 963 \times 10^2$	50	$9\ 815 \times 10^3$
B	628×10^2	200	$12\ 560 \times 10^3$

$\Sigma V = 2\ 519 \times 10^2$ $\Sigma Vx = 22\ 375 \times 10^3$

$$\Sigma V \bar{x} = \Sigma Vx$$
$$\bar{x} = \frac{\Sigma Vx}{\Sigma V}$$
$$= \frac{22\ 375 \times 10^3}{2\ 591 \times 10^2}$$
$$= \textbf{86·36 mm}$$

i.e. The centre of gravity of the shaft lies 86·36 mm from OY axis and, since the shaft is symmetrical, on the OX axis.

EXERCISES

1. Calculate the position of the centre of gravity for each of the shapes shown in Figs. 128a and 128b.

2. A crate containing various components has to be hoisted by a crane from the dockside to the hold of a ship.

   An outline of the position of each component in the crate and their masses is represented in Fig. 129.

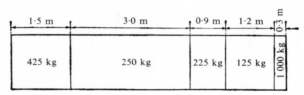

FIG. 129

Calculate the tension in the hoisting rope and its position relative to the length of the crate in order that the crate remains in a horizontal position.

The crate when empty has a mass of 280 kg.

3. Why is it desirable to keep the centre of gravity of a vehicle as low as possible?

   Find the position of the centre of gravity of a double-deck trolley bus given the following data:—

Unit	Weight (N)	Position of C.G. above ground level (mm)
Chassis	17.5×10^3	480
Motors, batteries, switch gear, etc.	42×10^3	400
Transmission	2.63×10^3	360
Coach work	21×10^3	1 200

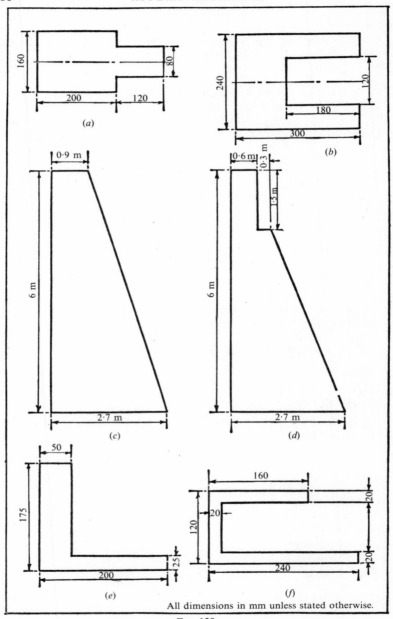

All dimensions in mm unless stated otherwise.

FIG. 128a

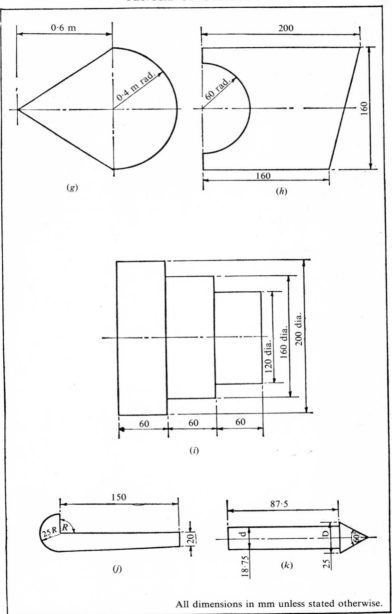

(g)

(h)

0·6 m

0·4 m rad.

200

60 rad.

160

160

(i)

200 dia.

160 dia.

120 dia.

60   60   60

(j)

150

25 R

R

20

(k)

87·5

d

D

60°

18·75

25

All dimensions in mm unless stated otherwise.

FIG. 128b

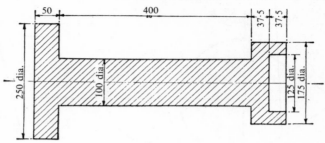

Fɪɢ. 130

4. A bar of mild steel is forged to the shape shown in Fig. 130. If the finished shaft is mounted in a single bearing, calculate the position of the centre line of this bearing from the left-hand end of the shaft. (Dimensions in mm.)

CHAPTER IV

FRAMED STRUCTURES

Any assembly of rods, bars, beams, etc., may be termed a frame structure. The joints of these structures are known as **nodes** and the individual rods or bars as **members.**

Such structures are designed to resist forces as in the case of bridges, roof trusses, cranes, etc. Our job is to find the part of the applied forces transmitted to the various members. In our calculations we make the following assumptions:—

(1) that the joints or nodes are pin joints;

(2) that all external forces are applied at joints;

(3) that each member can be represented by a straight line no matter the actual shape of its section;

(4) that each joint, and hence the whole structure, is in equilibrium;

(5) that friction in the joint is neglected.

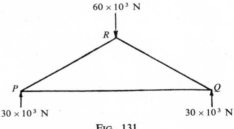

$$60 \times 10^3 \text{ N}$$

$$30 \times 10^3 \text{ N} \qquad 30 \times 10^3 \text{ N}$$

Fig. 131

The simple frame shown in Fig. 131 is in the form of an isosceles triangle. A force of 60×10^3 N is concentrated at the ridge R and, since the frame is isosceles, the supports P and Q must take an equal share of the force, i.e. each equal to 30×10^3 N.

Each member of this particular frame shares in supporting the applied force; the members RP and RQ are being compressed between the 60×10^3 N force and the 30×10^3 N supporting forces.

When a member is resisting a compressive force we say that it is in compression and it is called a **strut.**

83

Now, if the member *PQ* is removed, the structure will collapse—the points *P* and *Q* going away from each other. Therefore the ends of the member *PQ* are being pulled apart. A member resisting this pulling is said to be in tension and is called a **tie.**

To avoid destruction, when a member is subjected to a force, compressive or tensile, it resists the external force by an internal force of equal magnitude but opposite direction. These internal forces are the ones we wish to find.

Figs. 132 and 133 show two members, one in compression and the other in tension, and the graphical representation of each.

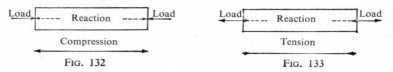

FIG. 132   FIG. 133

When the force has been found it can be used, along with the allowable stress for the material, to calculate the area of the section best suited to the structure being designed.

It has already been stated that the force in each member acts at a point. In practice this is not necessarily so. In the case of a riveted joint, for example, the force is dissipated throughout the joint elements and is a much smaller force than that calculated. A frame designed to the calculated forces will, therefore, be stronger than necessary.

Referring to Fig. 134, we find that each joint has three forces acting on it. The direction of each force and magnitude of one is known. We have, in fact, a triangle-of-forces problem at each joint.

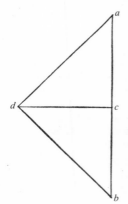

To help identify each member the position diagram is lettered using Bow's notation.

Inspection of the vector diagrams shows that the vector *cd* is common to both diagrams representing joints *P* and *Q*. It will be possible, then, to superimpose one diagram on the other with *cd* as the common factor. The vector diagram will now appear as shown in Fig. 135, thus:—(Fig. 135).

In the combined diagram the vector line *acb* appears as one straight line and it represents the magnitude and the direction of the applied force and the reactions at *P* and *Q*. (*bca*.)

FIG. 135

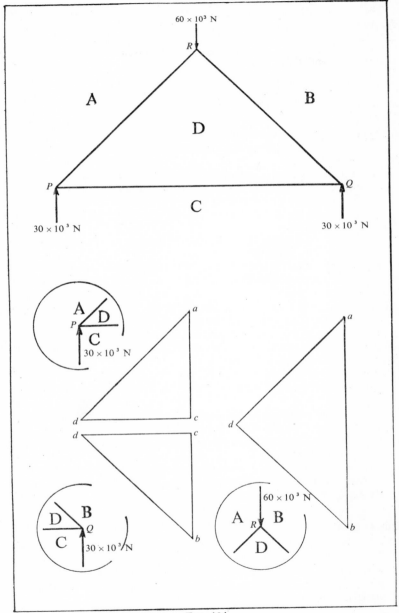

FIG. 134

This line is called the load line (the load measured in newtons), or the **external vector diagram** and where possible should be the first line of the vector diagram to be drawn.

When solving framed-structure problems the following procedure may be found useful:—

(1) draw the position of structure diagram to a suitable scale;
(2) letter the spaces using Bow's notation;
(3) calculate the reactions at the supports;
(4) draw the 'load line' in the vector diagram to a suitable scale;
(5) choose a suitable node (where the forces in not more than two members are unknown) and draw the polygon of forces for that node;
(6) transfer the direction arrows from the vector diagram to the respective members in the structure diagram (remove the arrows from the vector diagram);
(7) move on to another node, using a strut or tie found from a previous node;
(8) repeat stages 6 and 7 until all the members are represented in the vector diagram;
(9) complete the table of results. The table should have one line for each member and state its name, magnitude and nature (strut or tie);
(10) alternatively, the magnitude of the force in each member may be written alongside that member in the structure diagram.

The transfer of the direction arrows from the vector diagram to the structure diagram often gives rise to difficulty. This need not be so if one or two basic rules are applied.

1. Where possible always establish the first direction arrow for *each* polygon in the vector diagram from the given forces in the structure diagram.
2. When this is established ensure that all the other arrows follow each other round the polygon.
3. Transfer these arrows *immediately* back to the members of the joint being considered.
4. Arrow opposite ends of members in rule three. (Make sure these arrows are in opposite directions.)
5. Remove arrows from vector diagram.

Aids to good results

1. Always use a sharp pencil giving thin clear lines.
2. Ensure all lines are the exact scale length.
3. Keep arrow heads small and about 3 mm away from the joint.
. Keep the vector diagram on the same page of your book as the structure diagram.

5. When choosing a scale keep it as large and simple as possible.

Note:—A "just" rigid frame is a frame which, if one member is removed, will collapse completely or in part—e.g. a quadrilateral with one diagonal.

An "over rigid" frame has a surplus of members—e.g. a quadrilateral with both diagonals. Such problems cannot be solved at this stage unless the force in a particular member is given along with the forces produced by given loads. The number of members in a just-rigid frame is given by the formula $2n - 3$, where n is the number of joints in the frame.

Reactions

Where only one member is acting at a point, the reaction produced by it at the point is equal in magnitude and opposite in direction to the force acting in the member (Fig. 136).

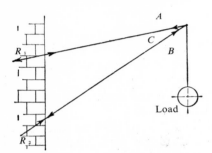

$$R_1 = ca, \quad R_2 = bc$$

Fig. 136

Where two or more members act at a point, the reaction produced by them is equal in magnitude and opposite in direction to the resultant of the forces in the members acting at the point (Fig. 137).

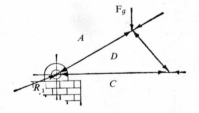

$$R_1 = ac$$
i.e. equilibrant of ad and dc

Fig. 137

Roller reactions

In structural work it is often necessary to give one or more of the supports of the framework restricted movement to allow for expansion and contraction, etc. To achieve this the frame is often mounted on a roller or rollers depending on the magnitude of the load it has to support.

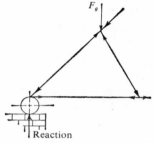

Fig. 138

When rollers are used in the design of a framed structure, the direction of the reaction between the rollers and the surface on which they are resting is always taken to be at right angles to the surface (Fig. 138).

Example 1.

Calculate the magnitude and nature of the force in each member of the frame shown. (Fig. 139).

Procedure

1. Draw the position diagram to a suitable scale.
2. Letter the spaces using Bow's notation.
3. Choose a scale for the vector diagram and draw the external vector line *ab* to represent the 1 340N force in magnitude and direction.
4. The triangle of forces can be drawn for the joint *ABD*. Through *a* draw *ad* parallel to *AD* and through *b* draw *bd* parallel to *BD*.
5. Lightly mark the direction arrows round triangle *abd*. The given force establishes the direction $a \rightarrow b$ and hence $b \rightarrow d \rightarrow c$.
6. Transfer these arrows back to the joint being considered. In this case the direction of *bd* is upwards, therefore the direction of the arrow on *BD* is upwards—i.e. toward the joint. Similarly the force in the member *AD* acts towards the joint.
7. Arrow the opposite ends of the members just finished with.
8. Measure the length of *bd* and, with the aid of the vector diagram scale, convert to a force. This force represents the magnitude of the force in the member *BD*. In the same way find the force in the member *AD*.
9. Through the point *d* draw a line parallel to member *DC*. Where this line cuts the vector line *ab*, gives the point *c*.
10. The position diagram shows both reactions to be vertical. The vector line *bc*, therefore, represents the magnitude of the reaction

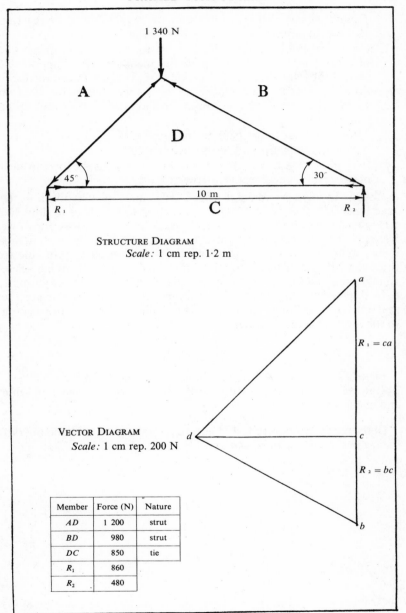

1 340 N

A

B

D

45°   30°

10 m

C

R_1 R_2

STRUCTURE DIAGRAM
Scale: 1 cm rep. 1·2 m

a

$R_1 = ca$

VECTOR DIAGRAM
Scale: 1 cm rep. 200 N

d   c

$R_2 = bc$

b

Member	Force (N)	Nature
AD	1 200	strut
BD	980	strut
DC	850	tie
R_1	860	
R_2	480	

FIG. 139

D

R_2 and the vector line *ca* represents the magnitude of the reaction R_1 and the directions are vertically upward.

11. From the information gained in 10 we can now establish the direction of the force acting in the member *DC*. Suppose we choose the joint *ADC*; the direction of R_1 is known to be vertically upward. Tracing the members at this joint in the vector diagram we find that the arrows go round the diagram (triangle *cad*) in the order $a \rightarrow d \rightarrow c$.

12. Transfer these arrows back to the joint *ADC*.

13. Arrow the opposite end of the member *DC*.

14. Prepare a table and tabulate the results—i.e. state the force in each member and whether it is a strut or a tie.

Note:—In this case we did not need to calculate the magnitude of the reactions since enough information was given to enable us to draw the triangle of forces for the joint *ABD*. Once this triangle was drawn we were able to establish the magnitude and direction of the forces acting in the members *BD* and *AD*. With this information we are able to draw the triangle of forces for the joints *ADC* and *BCD*. When these triangles are drawn the reactions R_1 and R_2 are automatically found.

In later examples, however, it may be necessary to calculate the reactions and complete the external force diagram before proceeding to the internal force diagram.

EXERCISES

Figs. 140–143 show four examples of typical frame problems. Following the procedure used in example 1, redraw **to your own scale** and check your results with those given.

Determine the magnitude and nature of the force in each member of the frames shown in Figs. 144 and 145.

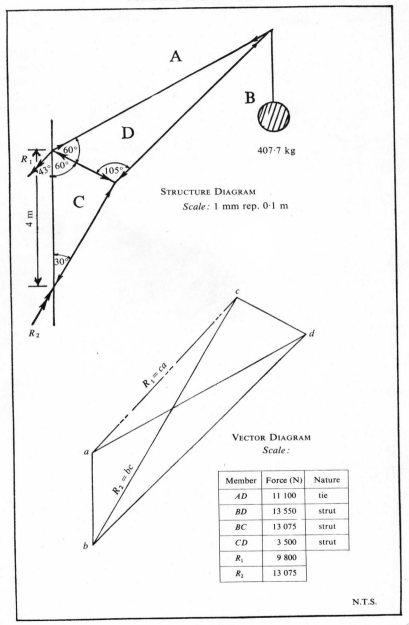

A

B

407·7 kg

D

R_1

60°

60°

43°

105°

C

4 m

30°

STRUCTURE DIAGRAM
Scale: 1 mm rep. 0·1 m

R_2

c

d

$R_1 = ca$

a

$R_2 = bc$

b

VECTOR DIAGRAM
Scale:

Member	Force (N)	Nature
AD	11 100	tie
BD	13 550	strut
BC	13 075	strut
CD	3 500	strut
R_1	9 800	
R_2	13 075	

N.T.S.

Fig. 140

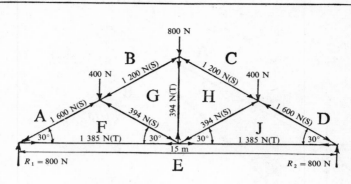

STRUCTURE DIAGRAM
Scale = 1 mm rep. 0·10 m

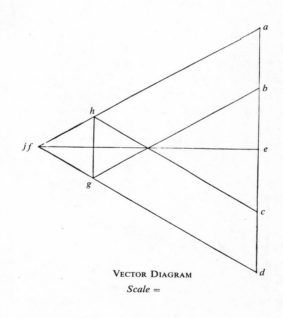

VECTOR DIAGRAM
Scale =

FIG. 141

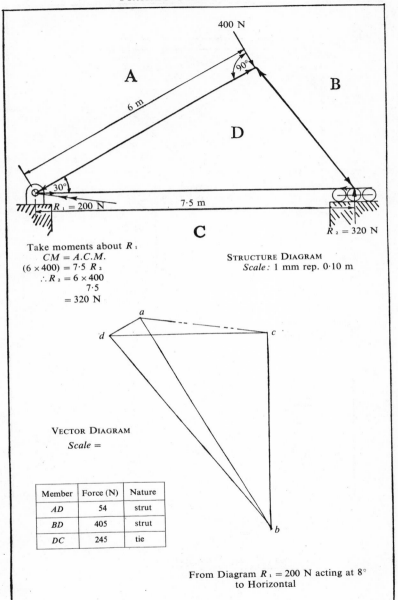

400 N

A

6 m

90°

B

D

30°

$R_1 = 200$ N

7·5 m

C

$R_2 = 320$ N

Take moments about R_1
$CM = A.C.M.$
$(6 \times 400) = 7 \cdot 5 \ R_2$
$\therefore R_2 = \dfrac{6 \times 400}{7 \cdot 5}$
$= 320$ N

STRUCTURE DIAGRAM
Scale: 1 mm rep. 0·10 m

a

d   c

b

VECTOR DIAGRAM
Scale =

Member	Force (N)	Nature
AD	54	strut
BD	405	strut
DC	245	tie

From Diagram $R_1 = 200$ N acting at 8°
to Horizontal

FIG. 142

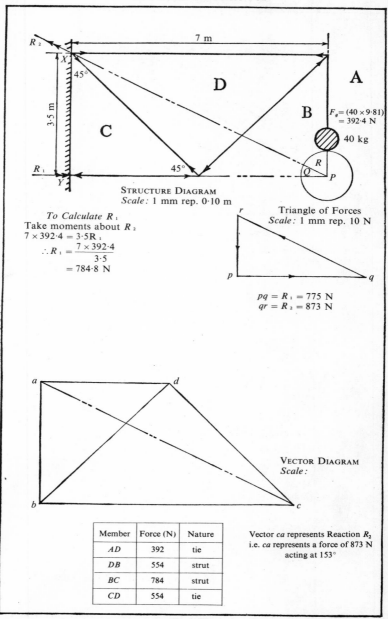

R_2

7 m

X

45°

3·5 m

D

A

B

$F_g = (40 \times 9.81)$
$= 392.4$ N

40 kg

C

R

R_1

45°

Q

P

Y

STRUCTURE DIAGRAM
Scale: 1 mm rep. 0·10 m

To Calculate R_1
Take moments about R_2
$7 \times 392.4 = 3.5 R_1$
$$\therefore R_1 = \frac{7 \times 392.4}{3.5}$$
$$= 784.8 \text{ N}$$

Triangle of Forces
Scale: 1 mm rep. 10 N

r

p

q

$pq = R_1 = 775$ N
$qr = R_2 = 873$ N

a

d

b

c

VECTOR DIAGRAM
Scale:

Member	Force (N)	Nature
AD	392	tie
DB	554	strut
BC	784	strut
CD	554	tie

Vector *ca* represents Reaction R_2
i.e. *ca* represents a force of 873 N
acting at 153°

FIG. 143

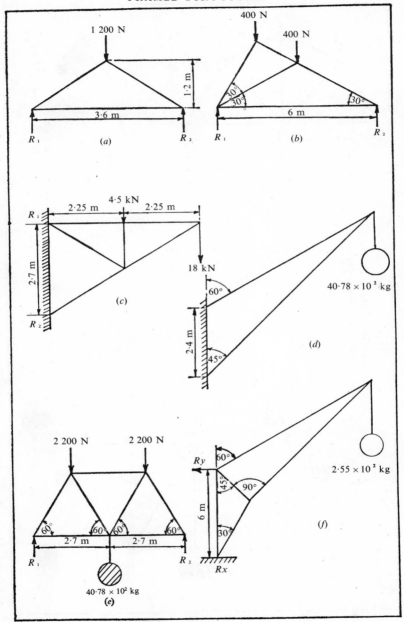

FIG. 144

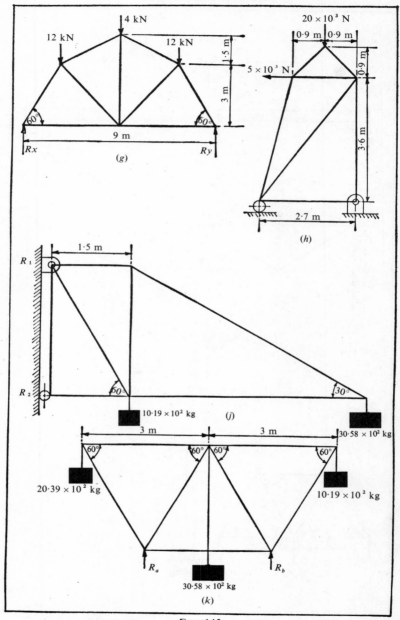

FIG. 145

CHAPTER V

FRICTION

In studying friction we examine various different pairs of dry surfaces to find out something about how one surface slides over another. Sometimes the surfaces slide very easily, as when the metal runners of a sledge slide over an icy surface. At other times, if the sledge rests on a dry road, the resistance to movement is greater and if two or three people sit on the sledge while it is resting on the dry road it is very difficult indeed to move the sledge.

Obviously there is some force acting between the surfaces in contact which affects the manner is which the surfaces slide. We will study this force and the conditions which affect it.

The first thing we notice about the force is that it always opposes motion. If you try to slide a piece of furniture across the floor you will find that you have to exert a force to move it, i.e. you have to overcome a resistance. If you then turn round and try to push it in the opposite direction you will find that the resistance still acts against you, and no matter which way you try to slide the body the resistance acts the opposite way.

When one surface slides or tends to slide over another surface a force is brought into play which opposes the movement. This force is the force of friction.

In the following experiment we will examine the way a body slides when the force causing sliding overcomes friction.

Experiment 1

Object:—To examine the way a body moves against a frictional resistance.

Apparatus:—A friction board, i.e. a wooden board with a pulley mounted at one end as shown (Fig. 146), a block of wood, string, a supply of small masses and a carrier.

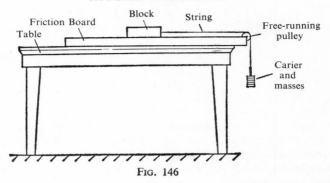

FIG. 146

Procedure:—Tie the string to the block, place the block on the friction board passing the string over the pulley, and tie the carrier to the free end of the string.

Add a small mass to the carrier to see if its weight will move the block. Keep adding small masses until the pulling force overcomes the friction between the block and the board and causes the block to slide. Watch carefully how the block slides.

Remove the last few masses so that the block rests on the board without moving. Add the masses gently one at a time and each time give the block a slight push to start it moving. When, on receiving a slight push, the block continues to move, note carefully how it moves.

Repeat the experiment using other blocks and note carefully how the block moves each time.

You will notice that the force which causes the block to start moving makes it gain speed after it has started, but that if the block is given a slight push to start it if a smaller force can keep it moving at constant speed.

Conclusions:—(1) The force which caused the block to start sliding also caused it to gain speed.

(2) When the block was given a slight push to start it moving, a smaller force kept it moving with constant speed.

Static and sliding friction

Now let us examine what happened in the last experiment.

We set the block on the board and applied a small force to make it slide. At first the force was balanced by the force of friction between the two surfaces and the block remained stationary. This is known as **static friction.**

As we added more small masses the increased weight increased the pulling force. The force of static friction also increased until it reached

the limit of static friction. This was the maximum value that static friction could reach, and when we added another small mass the sliding force was increased and overcame the static friction, causing the block to move.

After the block started to move there were two forces acting on it, a force pulling it and a force of friction opposing motion. When a body is moving like this, the friction opposing motion is known as **sliding or kinetic friction.**

If, after the block had started to move, the force causing sliding had balanced the kinetic friction force exactly, the block would have moved with uniform speed. We saw however, that the block gained speed, showing that the pulling force was greater than the force of kinetic friction.

Since this pulling force was necessary to overcome static friction it follows that the limit of static friction was higher than the value of sliding friction. In other words, it required a greater force to start the block moving than it required to keep it moving after it had started.

This can be explained when we examine the nature of the surfaces. No surface is ever perfectly smooth and a microscope can show roughness in surfaces which, to the naked eye, appear to be perfectly smooth. When the block is at rest the roughness on the surface of the block can sink into the roughness in the board so that it requires a considerable force to start it moving. When it does start to move the surfaces do not get time to settle together in a new position so that the force required to keep it moving is not so great.

You can get this effect on a large scale with two sheets of corrugated iron. Allow the top sheet to settle into the bottom sheet and then try to pull it against the corrugations. You will find that it requires a large force to pull it at the start, but, after it starts moving, if you do not allow it to settle into the next set of corrugations, the force required to keep it moving is not so great (Fig. 147).

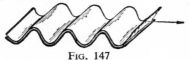

FIG. 147

The nature of the surfaces in contact

The force required to overcome friction and cause sliding varies very greatly with the nature of the surfaces in contact. For example, if you take two pieces of roughly sawn wood and try to slide one over the other you will find that it takes a considerable force, but if you plane both surfaces and try again you will find that the smoother surfaces will slide more easily.

This is only a qualitative result, but the effect of friction between the various contact surfaces will be studied more closely in the following experiment.

Experiment 2

Object:—To show that the friction between two surfaces depends on the nature of the surfaces and to find:—

    (*a*) the limit of static friction; and

    (*b*) the sliding friction between various pairs of surfaces in contact.

Apparatus:—A friction board, carrier and supply of small masses, a strip of linoleum, paper, and a sheet of glass, all large enough to cover the friction board.

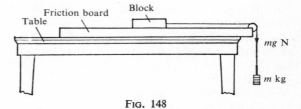

FIG. 148

Procedure:—With the apparatus set up as shown in Fig. 148 add a small mass to the carrier at *m*. Give the block a slight push and see if it continues to slide. If it does not, add another small mass at *m* and give the block a slight push. Continue adding small masses at *m* until, on receiving a slight push, the block continues to slide at constant speed along the board. When this happens it means that the pulling force *mg* is just balancing the sliding friction. Note the result.

Replace the block on the board and continue adding masses at *m* but this time do not push the block after adding each mass. Find the force required to start the block moving from rest, i.e. the force required to overcome the static friction.

This gives the sliding friction and the limit of static friction for the two wood surfaces.

Pin a strip of paper to the surface of the board and repeat the experiment with wood against paper.

Pin paper to the block and repeat the experiment with a sheet of glass on the board.

Vary the pairs of surfaces as often as you like using the materials at hand. Tabulate your results as shown.

Results

Surfaces in Contact	Static Friction ~ F_s	Sliding Friction ~ F_k
Wood on Wood		
Wood on Paper		
Paper on Paper		
Wood on Linoleum		
Wood on Glass		
etc. etc.		

Conclusion:—The friction between two surfaces depends on the nature of the surfaces in contact.

Area of surfaces in contact

When doing the last experiment you probably wondered what the effect would be of turning the block on its side. This might alter the area of the surfaces in contact and might have an effect on the friction between the surfaces. We will investigate this in the next experiment.

Experiment 3

Object:—To find if the friction between two surfaces depends on the area of the surfaces in contact.

Apparatus:—A friction board, several rectangular blocks, masses and carrier, a strip of linoleum, paper, glass, etc.

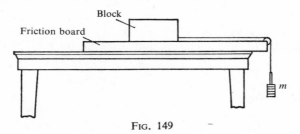

Fig. 149

Procedure:—Set up the friction board as before and, with the largest surface of the block in contact with the board, find the sliding and static friction between the block and the board. Measure the length and breadth of the block and so find the area of the surfaces in contact.

Turn the block on its edge as shown in Fig. 149, and find the sliding and static friction for the block and board in this position. Measure the block again and find the area of the surfaces now in contact. Repeat the experiment using other blocks and other surfaces on the board. Tabulate the results.

Nature of surfaces	Area of surface in contact (mm²)	Fs	Fk

Conclusion:—The friction between two surfaces is independent of the area of the surfaces in contact.

The reaction between the surfaces in contact

The effect of the reaction between the surfaces on the friction force may be demonstrated in the following way. Take hold of a chair and slide it across the floor. Now get someone to sit on the chair and again slide it across the floor. You will find it much harder to move the chair the second time because the reaction between the chair and the floor has been increased.

In the following experiment we will measure the exact relationship between the friction force and the reaction between the surfaces.

Experiment 4

Object:—To examine the relationship between the friction force and the reaction between surfaces in contact.

Apparatus:—A friction board, block, supply of small masses and carrier, supply of larger masses and a spring balance graduated in newtons.

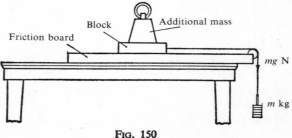

FIG. 150

Procedure:—Weigh the block on the spring balance, place it on the board and find the sliding friction and the limit of static friction between the block and the board.

Place a 0·5 kg mass on the block and again find the sliding and static friction between the block and the board.

Repeat this using 1 kg, 2 kg and 3 kg masses on the block and note your results in a tabular form.

The reaction between the surfaces is equal to the weight of the block *plus* the weight of the mass resting on it.

Results

Weight of block (N)	Mass added (kg)	Weight of added mass (N)	Reaction R (N)	Static friction force Fs (N)	Kinetic friction force Fk (N)	$\dfrac{Fs}{R}$	$\dfrac{Fk}{R}$

If you carry out your experiment carefully you will find that as the reaction between the surfaces increases the friction force increases in proportion so that the ratio

$$\frac{F}{R} = \text{a constant}$$

This constant is known as the **coefficient of friction** for the pair of surfaces in contact and is denoted by the Greek letter μ (mu).

Thus $F/R = \mu$ for any pair of surfaces

$$\text{or } F = \mu R$$

We use μ as the coefficient of static friction where we are dealing with a stationary body and as the coefficient of kinetic friction when dealing with a sliding body.

Coefficient of friction

If F_s is the frictional resistance when a body is on the point of sliding along a surface and R is the perpendicular reaction between the surfaces the coefficient of static friction $= F_s/R$.

If F_k is the frictional resistance when a body is sliding with uniform speed over a surface and R is the perpendicular reaction between the surfaces then the coefficient of kinetic friction $= F_k/R$.

Laws of friction—for dry surfaces

The experiments we have conducted may be summarised as follows:
1. Friction always opposes motion.
2. The friction between two surfaces depends on the nature of the surfaces in contact.
3. Friction is independent of the area of the surfaces in contact.
4. Friction, both sliding and static, is directly proportional to the reaction between the surfaces.

These findings are known as the **laws of friction.**

Example 1

A wooden packing case and its contents have a mass of 25 kg. Find the force required to move it over a floor if the coefficient of static friction between the case and the floor is 0·48.

$F = ?$ $F = \mu R$

$\mu = 0·48$ $= 0·48 \times 245$

$R = 25 \times 9·81 = 245 \text{ N}$ $= 117·5$

$\therefore$ **Force necessary to move the case $= 117·5$ N**

Example 2

It requires a force of 20 N to pull a boy on his sledge over ice at constant speed. If the sledge has a mass of 6 kg and the coefficient of sliding friction between the surfaces is 0·041, find the mass of the boy.

$F = 20 \text{ N}$ $F = \mu R$

$\mu = 0·041$ $20 = 0·041 \times R$

$R = ?$ $\therefore R = \textbf{488 N}$

$\therefore$ Total weight $= 488$ N

$$\text{Total mass} = \frac{488}{9·81} = 49·8 \text{ kg}$$

$\therefore$ mass of boy $= 49·8 - 6 = \textbf{43·8 kg}$

Example 3

The force necessary to move the tailstock of a lathe over the machine bed at constant speed is 16 N. If the tailstock itself has a mass of 15 kg calculate the coefficient of sliding friction between the surfaces in contact.

$F = 16 \text{ N}$ $F = \mu R$

$\mu = ?$ $16 = \mu \times 147$

$R = 15 \times 9·81 = 147 \text{ N}$ $\therefore \mu = 0·109$

$\therefore$ **Coefficient of friction $= 0·109$**

Tractive resistance

So far we have dealt only with problems of sliding; but in engineering we often have to deal with friction in a different form, for example, when hauling a railway wagon.

If the wheels were locked it would be a pure sliding problem but, if the wheels are allowed to roll, the pulling force required will be very much less. There will still be friction at the wheel bearings and between the wheel flanges and the rails, etc., but the laws of sliding friction will not apply.

In this case we take all the resistances together and call them **tractive resistance.**

Now obviously the force required to pull the wagon will increase as the wagon is loaded, since friction at the bearings will increase, so that in our calculations we must consider the weight of the wagon and its load.

The tractive resistance is generally found by experiment and is usually expressed in newtons/kilogram, e.g. if the tractive resistance is 0·05 N/kg and the wagon has a mass of 4 000 kg then force resisting motion = 0·05 × 4 000 = **200 N.**

The T.R. may also be expressed as 50 N/Mg or 50 N/tonne and the mass of the wagon given as 4 Mg or tonnes. In this case

Force resisting motion = 50 × 4 = **200 N.**

Example 1

A railway engine has a mass of 75 Mg. Find the force required to drive the engine against a tractive resistance of 70 N/Mg.

Driving force required = mass of engine × tractive resistance

= 75 × 70

= **5 250 N**

If the engine is pulling a train of 6 coaches, each coach of mass 30 Mg, find the pull in the draw-bar between the engine and the first coach, assuming the same tractive resistance.

Total mass of 6 coaches = 6 × 30

= **180 Mg**

Force required at the draw-bar = mass of coaches × tractive resistance

= 180 × 70

= **12 600 N**

Friction on an inclined plane

When we were dealing with a body resting on an inclined plane, we found that the weight of the body could be resolved into two components—one of which tended to make the body slide down the plane and the other at right angles to the plane giving the normal reaction between the plane and the body.

Now if the angle of inclination θ (Fig. 151) is very small, the force acting down the plane ($mg \sin \theta$) will not be great enough to overcome friction and cause the body to slide, but if we increase the angle θ by tilting the plane the force $mg \sin \theta$ will increase until it overcomes friction and the body starts to slide.

The angle at which the body is just on the point of sliding is known as the **angle of friction** or the **angle of repose**.

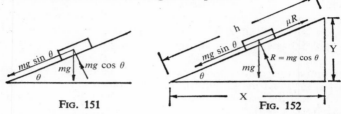

FIG. 151   FIG. 152

Let us consider the position when the body is just about to slide (Fig. 152).

Let the sloping length of the plane be h, the horizontal length be x and the vertical height be y.

Force acting down the plane

$$= mg \sin \theta$$

$$= mg \times \frac{y}{h}$$

Reaction between the plane and the body

$$= mg \cos \theta$$

$$= mg \times \frac{x}{h}$$

Friction force resisting motion

$$= \mu R$$

$$= \mu mg \cos \theta$$

$$= \mu mg \frac{x}{h}$$

But if the body is just about to slide these two forces balance, then

$$mg \sin \theta = \mu R$$

i.e.

$$mg \frac{y}{h} = \mu mg \frac{x}{h}$$

$$y = \mu x$$

$$\mu = \frac{y}{x} = \tan \theta$$

So that, if the body is just on the point of sliding, the coefficient of friction will be equal to the tangent of the angle of friction.

Let us see if this holds good in practice.

Experiment 5

Object: To compare the coefficient of static friction between two surfaces with the tangent of the angle of friction.

Apparatus: A hinged board fitted with a quadrant and lock-nut, a wooden block, a supply of small masses and carrier and a protractor.

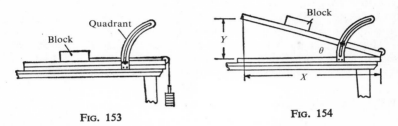

FIG. 153   FIG. 154

Procedure:—Weigh the block, and with the friction board horizontal (Fig. 153) find the force of sliding friction and the limit of static friction between the board and the block. Calculate the coefficients of sliding and static friction.

Remove the masses and string from the block and again set the block on the board. Raise the hinged board very slowly until the block starts to slide down. Lock the board in this position (Fig. 154) with the lock-nut. Using the protractor measure the angle θ between the two boards and from a book of trigonometric tables look up the tangent of the angle.

Check the tangent by measuring the vertical height of the plane (y) and the horizontal length (x) and calculating

$$\tan \theta = \frac{y}{x}$$

Compare the tangent of the angle with the coefficient of static friction.

Unlock the nut and lower the board slightly. Find the angle at which the block will slide with constant speed on being given a slight push. Lock the board in this position. This gives the angle of sliding friction. Again measure θ, x, and y and find the tangent of the angle of sliding friction. Compare this with the coefficient of sliding friction.

The experiment can be repeated varying the surfaces in contact.

Motion on the inclined plane

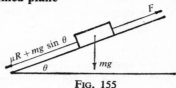

Fig. 155

Before a body will move on an incline, it is necessary to overcome friction. Since friction always opposes motion, the body will move if force F (Fig. 155), parallel to the plane, overcomes friction and the gravity component down the plane ($mg \sin \theta$).

Hence the body will move up the plane if force F is greater than $mg \sin \theta +$ friction.

$$\text{The force of friction} = \mu R \qquad \text{where } R = mg \cos \theta$$
$$\therefore F = \mu mg \cos \theta$$

When the body is just about to move

$$F = mg \sin \theta + \mu mg \cos \theta$$

Similarly when F is acting down the plane the body will be about to move when

$$F = \mu mg \cos\theta - mg \sin \theta$$

Example.

A boat of mass 800 kg rests on a concrete slipway inclined at an angle of 15° to the horizontal. If the coefficient of friction between the keel and the concrete is 0·6, find the force required to slide the boat down into the water.

Pulling force required

$= \text{frictional force} - \text{force down the plane}$

$= \mu R - mg \sin 15°$

$= \mu mg \cos \theta - mg \sin 15°$

$= (0·6 \times 800 \times 9·81 \times 0·965\,9) - (800 \times 9·81 \times 0·258\,8)$

$= 4\,540 - 2\,030$

$= \mathbf{2\,510\ N}$

Force inclined to the horizontal

If a body resting on a horizontal plane is acted on by a force which is inclined to the plane, then only part of the force is going to be used to overcome friction; the other part being used to increase or decrease the reaction between the surfaces.

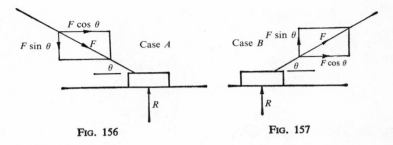

Fig. 156   Fig. 157

In case *A* (Fig. 156), where the force *F* is acting at an angle θ to the horizontal, on a block of mass *m*, force *F* may be resolved into a horizontal component $F \cos \theta$ and a vertical component $F \sin \theta$.

Since the vertical component increases the reaction between the surfaces the reaction becomes

$$R = mg + F \sin \theta$$

and in case *B* (Fig. 157), where the force *F* acts in an upward direction,

$$R = mg - F \sin \theta$$

Since the horizontal component tending to cause sliding is $F \cos \theta$, the block will move if:—

$F \cos \theta$ is greater than $\mu(mg + F \sin\theta)$ in case *A*,

and $F \cos \theta$ is greater than $\mu(mg - F \sin \theta)$ in case *B*.

Example 1.

A crate is pushed across a horizontal floor with a force inclined at an angle of 45° (Fig. 158). If the crate and its contents has a mass of 200 kg find the magnitude of the force. (Coefficient of friction between the floor and the crate = 0·4.)

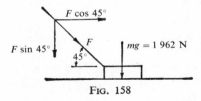

Fig. 158

Total reaction on floor $= R = mg + F \sin 45°$

$$= 1\ 962 + 0.707\ F \text{ N}$$

Force causing motion $\qquad = F \cos 45°$

Force to overcome friction $= \mu R$

i.e. $$F \cos 45° = 0\cdot4(1\ 962 + 0\cdot707\ F)$$
$$\therefore 0\cdot707\ F = 784\cdot8 + 0\cdot283\ F$$
$$\therefore 0\cdot424\ F = 784\cdot8$$
$$\therefore F = \frac{784\cdot8}{0\cdot424}$$
$$= 1\ 850\ N$$

The force inclined to an inclined plane

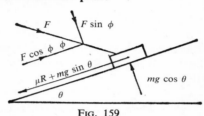

FIG. 159

We often find that the force acting on the body is not parallel to the plane.

Consider the body at rest on an inclined plane and acted on by a force F at an angle ϕ to the plane (Fig. 159).

The force F may be resolved into two components, one acting parallel to the plane and the other perpendicular to the plane. The component parallel to the plane will supply a force of $F \cos \phi$ acting up the plane and the component perpendicular to the plane will increase the reaction between the block and the plane by $F \sin \phi$.

i.e. the total reaction between the block and the plane, R,
$$= mg \cos \theta + F \sin \phi$$
and this reaction will have to be used when calculating the friction force μR

Since friction always opposes motion, the block will move up the plane if $F \cos \phi$ is greater than
$$mg \sin \theta + \mu(mg \cos \theta + F \sin \phi)$$
and will move down the plane if $mg \sin \theta$ is greater than
$$F \cos \phi + \mu(mg \cos \theta + F \sin \phi)$$
Similarly, when force F pulls the body up the plane, acting away from the plane at an angle ϕ, the total reaction between the block and the plane, R,
$$= mg \cos \theta - F \sin \phi$$

and the block will move up the plane if $F \cos \phi$ is greater than
$$mg \sin \theta + \mu(mg \cos \theta - F \sin \phi)$$
and will move down the plane if $mg \sin \theta$ is greater than
$$F \cos \phi + \mu(mg \cos \theta - F \sin \phi)$$
N.B. If force F is horizontal, angle θ is equal to angle ϕ (alternate angles) and the calculation is similar to the above.

Example

A tractor is used to drag a log of mass 400 kg up an incline of 12°. If the tow rope makes an angle of 15° with the incline, find the tension in the rope. (The coefficient of friction between the log and the ground is 0·45.)

Let the tension in the rope be T N.

Component of the force acting parallel to the plane $= T \cos 15°$.

Reaction between the log and the plane $= mg \cos 12° - T \sin 15°$.

When the log is about to move up the plane, dragging force parallel to the plane = component of the weight acting down the plane + friction.

$$T \cos 15° = mg \sin 12° + \mu R$$
$$T \cos 15° = mg \sin 12° + \mu \,(mg \cos 12° - T \sin 15°)$$
$$0.965\ 9T = 7\ 848 \times 0.207\ 9 + 0.45\ (7\ 848 \times 0.978\ 1) - T \times 0.258\ 8)$$
$$0.965\ 9T = 1\ 630 + 0.45\ (7\ 680 - 0.258\ 8T)$$
$$= 1\ 630 + 3\ 450 - 0.116\ 4T$$
$$1.08T = 5\ 084$$
$$T = 4\ 710$$

∴ Tension in the rope = **4 710** *N*.

Application of friction to brakes

The diagram (Fig. 160) shows a brake acting on a wheel or a brake drum. The metal brake shoe carries a brake lining (usually made of an asbestos compound), fastened with copper or aluminium rivets sunk below the rubbing surface.

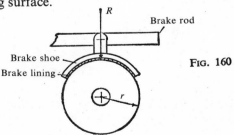

FIG. 160

The brake rod supplies the force pressing the lining against the brake drum. The force causing motion is supplied through the axle and the force supplied by the brake rod gives the reaction between the surfaces.

As earlier experiments showed, friction is independent of the area of surfaces in contact and, therefore, the area of brake lining does not affect the braking force but, in practice, the linings are made as large as practicable to reduce wear.

Let the co-efficient of friction between the brake drum and lining be μ, then:— the tangential force at the circumference tending to stop motion $= \mu R$, and braking torque $= \mu R r$ (where $r =$ radius of the brake drum).

If the reaction is measured in newtons and the radius of the wheel in metres, the braking torque is in newton metres (Nm).

Example

Calculate the friction torque exerted by the brake shown in Fig. 161 if the coefficient of friction between the brake lining and the wheel is 0·72.

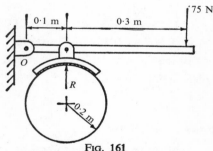

FIG. 161

Let the reaction between the brake lining and the wheel be R N. Take moments about O

$$0\cdot1 \times R = 75 \times 0\cdot4$$

$$R = 300 \text{ N}$$

$$\text{Friction torque} = \mu R r$$

$$= 0\cdot72 \times 300 \times 0\cdot2$$

$$= \textbf{43·2 Nm}$$

Friction in bearings

Steel shafts are generally run in bearings made of brass, whitemetal, or other low friction material, the shell of the metal being supported by the bearing block.

The diagram shows the bottom half of such a bearing carrying a shaft (Fig. 162).

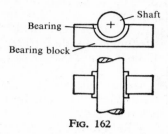

FIG. 162

Since the friction force is independent of the area of the surfaces in contact we need not consider the area of bearing surface.

If the coefficient of friction between the shaft and the bearing is μ, then:—

Friction force resisting motion,

$$F = \mu R$$

where R is the weight of the shaft plus any loads carried by it (pulleys etc.) and friction torque $= \mu Rr$ where r is the radius of the shaft.

Example 1

The shaft shown in Fig. 163 carries a pulley of mass 150 kg at its mid point. If the coefficient of friction between the shaft and the bearing surface is 0·07 and the radius of the shaft is 25 mm find the friction torque on the shaft at each bearing.

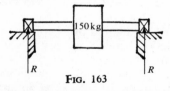

FIG. 163

Since the load on the pulley is equally distributed between the two bearings,

$$\text{load on each bearing} = \frac{150 \times 9\cdot81}{2}$$

friction torque at each bearing $= \mu Rr$

$$= 0\cdot07 \times \frac{150 \times 9\cdot81}{2} \times 0\cdot025$$

$$= 1\cdot29 \text{ Nm}$$

EXERCISES

1. A block of wood of mass 10 kg rests on a horizontal steel saw table. If it requires a force of 8 N to start the wood sliding, find the coefficient of limiting friction between the wood and the metal.

2. A force of 90 N is required to slide a packing case over a floor at constant speed. If the case has a mass of 44 kg, find the coefficient of sliding friction.

3. Find the force required to slide a metal casting of mass 35 kg across a bench if the coefficient of limiting friction between the casting and the bench is 0·3.

4. If it requires a pull of 30 N to drag an empty box of mass 15 kg across a floor, what dragging force would be necessary if the box contained a mass of 20 kg?

5. The slide valve of a steam engine (Fig. 164) has an area of 7 000 mm^2. Find the force required to move the valve if the steam pressure is 500 kN/m^2 and the coefficient of friction between the valve and the guides is 0·04.

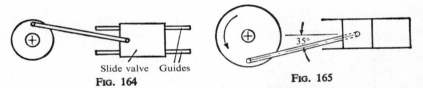

Slide valve   Guides
Fig. 164   **Fig. 165**

6. A box of mass 50 kg resting on a concrete floor has to be pulled by a rope inclined at 30° to the floor. If the coefficient of friction between the box and the floor is 0·3, find the pull required in the rope.

7. Fig. 165 shows the crank and piston of an air compressor. If the coefficient of friction between the piston and the cylinder wall is 0·03 and the force in the connecting rod is 60 N, find the force on the gas in the cylinder. Neglect the mass of the piston.

8. A platform in a loading bay slopes at an angle of 25°. Find the force required to drag a packing case of mass 70 kg up the slope if the coefficient of friction between the case and the slope is 0·55.

9. A body of mass 25 kg rests on a plane inclined at an angle of 30° to the horizontal. Find the force required to hold the body at rest
   (a) if the force acts parallel to the plane
   (b) if the force is horizontal
   The coefficient of friction between the body and the plane is 0·43.

10. It is found by experiment that the force required to slide a bag of flour of mass 50 kg over a smooth wooden chute is 120 N. Find

the angle at which the chute must be constructed so that the bag will slide freely under the action of gravity.

11. Find the force required to pull a train of 10 wagons up an incline of 1 in 15 if each wagon has a mass of 1 600 kg and the tractive resistance is 15 N/tonne.

12. A lorry of mass 2·5 tonnes coasts freely at constant speed down an incline of 1 in 140 while carrying a mass of 5 tonnes of coal. Find the tractive resistance to the motion of the lorry.

13. An electric motor of mass 450 kg has to be unloaded from a lorry by drawing it down a wooden ramp. The lorry platform is 1·5 m high and the ramp is 4 m long. Find the force required to slide the motor down the ramp if the coefficient of friction between the wood and the motor is 0·50.

14. A ship of mass 5 000 tonnes is launched from a slipway inclined at 20° to the horizontal. If the coefficient of friction between the slipway and the ship is 0·18, find the resisting force in the drag chains if the ship has to slide with constant speed.

15. A brake shoe presses on the brake drum of a wheel with a force of 60 N. If the coefficient of friction between the brake lining and the metal of the drum is 0·6 and the diameter of the drum is 300 mm, find the friction torque on the axle.

16. Fig. 166 shows the arrangement of a foot brake on a machine. If a force of 30 N acts vertically on the pedal, find the torque on the brake drum. The coefficient of friction between the brake lining and the drum is 0·72.

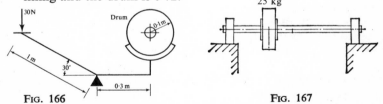

FIG. 166   FIG. 167

17. In an electric motor four carbon brushes are pressed against the commutator by springs each exerting a force of 0·8 N. If the commutator is 150 mm in diameter and the coefficient of friction between the brushes and the copper commutator is 0·13, find the friction torque resisting motion.

18. Fig. 167 shows a 50 mm diameter shaft, 1·25 m long and of mass 20 kg. If the shaft carries a pulley of mass 25 kg 150 mm from one end, find the coefficient of friction between the bearing metal and the shaft if the friction torque on the shaft has not to exceed 0·9 Nm.

CHAPTER VI

WORK, ENERGY AND POWER

Work

Most people have a general idea of what "work" is. For instance, if you go out and dig the garden, if you shovel coal from one position to another, if you push a wheelbarrow up a steep slope, if you drag a heavy log out of a field, you are "working" or "doing work".

Now let us examine one of these cases more closely. Suppose you have to drag a log out of a field. This may be "hard work' or it may be very easy—it depends on the size of the log. If it is a small sapling, you walk into the field, tie your rope to it and drag it away without much effort. If it is a large heavy log you have to haul heavily on your rope and you have to do a considerably greater amount of work to drag it away.

You will see from this that the amount of work you have to do depends on the force you have to exert.

Now if the log were lying just a few feet inside the gate, you would do a certain amount of work dragging it to the gate, but if the same log happened to be at the other side of the field you would find that you would have to do a greater amount of work dragging it across to the gate.

This shows that the amount of work depends on the distance through which you exert the force.

Now suppose the farmer had agreed to pay you a sum of money to get rid of the log from the field and you had toiled all day trying to shift it but you had failed. When he came to inspect the result of your exertions he would tell you that you had done no work and refuse to pay you, as the tree would still be in its original position. You would tell him you had used all your strength but the results would show that you had done no work. So you will see that no matter how great a force is exerted, **unless it causes movement it does no work.**

Imagine the log now to be caught in a rut (Fig. 168). You pull it at an angle to the rut as you make towards the gate, but the log slides along the rut despite your inclined pulling force. The pulling force F

116

can be resolved into two components, one acting in the direction of the rut and the other at right angles to it.

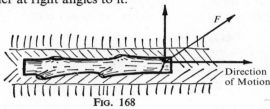

FIG. 168

Now, since the force at right angles to the rut is causing no movement in that direction it is doing no work. Only the component of the force acting in the direction of motion does the work.

When a force overcomes a resistance and causes motion, the component of the force in the direction of the motion is said to do work.

Normally we try to arrange our working force in the direction in which we want motion to take place since this is the most efficient way of using force.

Measuring work

Work depends on two things:—
1. The magnitude of the working force;
2. The distance through which the force acts.

We measure the magnitude of our force in newtons since the unit of force is the newton, and we measure the distance in metres since the unit of distance is the metre.

If we take one unit of force acting through one unit of distance, we get one unit of work, and, since the force is 1 N and the distance is 1 m, the unit of work is called one newton metre or 1 **joule** after James Prescott Joule who was one of the early investigators of this work.

One joule is the amount of work done when a force of 1 newton acts through a distance of 1 metre.

So that, if a force of 2 N acts through 1m, work done = 2 J

„	2 N	„	2 m	„	= 4 J
„	3 N	„	3 m	„	= 9 J
„	F N	„	D m	„	= $F \times D$ J

i.e. work done (J) by the force = force (N) × distance (m)

Example 1.

A hoist raises a 160 kg mass of cement to the top of a 10 m building. Find the work done in raising the load.

$$\text{Work done} = \text{force} \times \text{distance} = mg \times 10$$
$$= 160 \times 9\cdot81 \times 10$$
$$= \textbf{15 696 J}$$

Example 2.

Find the work done in raising 8 cubic metres of water from a reservoir 6 m below ground level. (1 m^3 of water has a mass of 1 000 kg).

$$\text{Mass of water} = 8\ 000 \text{ kg}$$
$$\text{Weight of water raised} = 8\ 000 \times 9 \cdot 81$$
$$= 78\ 480 \text{ N}$$

$$\text{Work done} = \text{force} \times \text{distance}$$
$$= 78\ 480 \times 6$$
$$= \textbf{470 880 J}$$

Example 3.

A wagon is pulled 60 metres along a railway track by a rope inclined at 30° to the track (Fig. 169). If the tension in the rope is 2 000 N, find the work done on the wagon.

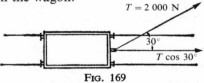

Fig. 169

The work is done by the component of the force acting *in the direction of motion.*

$$\therefore \text{ work done} = \text{working force} \times \text{distance}$$
$$= 2\ 000 \cos 30° \times 60$$
$$= 2\ 000 \times 0 \cdot 866 \times 60$$
$$= \textbf{103 920 J}$$

Energy

When we say that a body possesses energy we mean that it has a capacity to do work.

Energy exists in various forms and any one form of energy can be transformed into any other form of energy. Some forms of energy are, heat, light, electrical energy, chemical energy, mechanical energy, potential energy (the energy a body possesses due to its position), and kinetic energy (the energy a body possesses due to its motion).

A good example of how energy may be transformed is a hydro-electric plant.

The water in a high reservoir has potential energy. As it flows down a pipe to the turbine house the potential energy is changed into kinetic energy. The kinetic energy of the water drives the turbine to give mechanical energy which in turn drives generators to give electrical energy. The electrical energy goes into homes and factories where it is turned into heat, light, sound and mechanical energy.

Power

In our work in engineering we will often have to design engines to do certain tasks such as hauling trucks, pumping water, etc. and it is important to design the engine so that it is quite capable of doing all that is required of it. It is important too that the engine should be able to do the job in a reasonable length of time. For example, a small engine driving a pump might be able to empty a tank of water below ground level in half a day but we might want it emptied in half an hour. The solution would be, of course, to get a bigger pump and a more powerful engine. By "more powerful" we mean, in this case, an engine which could do the same amount of work but in less time. Thus in measuring the power of an engine we require to take account of the work done and the time taken to do the work.

In every subject if we wish to measure anything, we require a unit and the unit of power is taken as being the capacity to do one unit of work in one unit of time. The unit of work is, of course, the joule and the unit of time is the second so that the unit of power is the capacity to do one joule of work in one second of time. This unit of power is called the **watt** after James Watt one of the early pioneers of the steam engine and the watt is a rate of working of one joule per second.

Thus if a force of 50 newtons pushes a truck 10 metres along a track in 25 seconds then

$$\text{Total work done} = \text{force} \times \text{distance}$$
$$= 50 \times 10 = 500 \text{ J}$$
$$\text{Work done per second} = \frac{500}{25} = 20 \text{ J}$$

But one watt is the rate of working of one joule/second and this force did 20 joules/second

$$\text{Power developed} = 20 \text{ watts}$$

Example 1.

Find the power of an engine required to raise a load of 3 000 kg up a pit shaft 30 m deep in 5 minutes. (Neglect the weight of the rope.)

$$\text{Work done} = \text{force} \times \text{distance} = 3\,000 \times 9 \cdot 81 \times 30 \text{ J}$$
$$\text{Work done} = \frac{3\,000 \times 9 \cdot 81 \times 30}{5 \times 60} \text{ joules per second}$$
$$= \textbf{2 943 J/s}$$
$$\therefore \text{ Power required} = \textbf{2 943 W}$$

Example 2.

Find the power required to move a railway truck of mass 18 000 kg a distance of 2 km against a tractive resistance of 0·04 N/kg in 30 minutes.

$$\begin{aligned}
\text{Force resisting motion} &= \text{Mass of truck} \times \text{tractive} \\
\text{of the truck} & \qquad \text{resistance} \\
&= 18\,000 \times 0\text{·}04 \\
&= \mathbf{720\ N}
\end{aligned}$$

Distance moved by the truck $= 2\,000$ m

$$\begin{aligned}
\text{Total work done} &= \text{force} \times \text{distance} \\
&= 720 \times 2\,000 \\
\text{Work done per second} &= \frac{720 \times 2\,000}{30 \times 60} \\
&= 800\ \text{J}
\end{aligned}$$

$\therefore$ Power required $= \mathbf{800\ W}$

Example 3.

How long would it take a 2 kW pumping engine to raise 3 000 litres of water from a reservoir 15 m below ground level? (1 litre of water has a mass of 1 kg.)

$$\begin{aligned}
\text{Total work to be done} &= \text{Force} \times \text{distance} \\
&= 3\,000 \times 9\text{·}81 \times 15\ \text{J}
\end{aligned}$$

Power of the pump $= 2$ kW

i.e. pump works at a rate of 2 000 J per second

$$\begin{aligned}
\text{Time required} &= \frac{\text{total work to be done}}{\text{work done per second}} \\
&= \frac{3\,000 \times 9\text{·}81 \times 15}{2\,000} \\
&= 220\ \text{s} \\
&= \mathbf{3\ minutes\ 40\ seconds}
\end{aligned}$$

Converting kilometres per hour to metres per second

Sometimes we are given the speed of a truck in kilometres per hour (km/h). This is very useful in everyday life but we cannot use it in this form in our calculations since our units have to be in metres and seconds.

Now suppose a car is travelling at 36 km/h

$$\text{i.e. speed} = 36 \text{ km in 1 hour}$$
$$= 36 \times 1\,000 \text{ m in one hour}$$
$$= \frac{36 \times 1\,000}{60 \times 60} \text{ m/s}$$
$$= \textbf{10 m/s}$$

i.e. a speed of 36 km/h = 10 m/s
$$1 \text{ km/h} = \frac{10}{36} \text{ m/s}$$

If you remember this ratio you may use it to change speed in km/h to m/s.

Example 1.

Express 32 km/h in metres per second.

$$36 \text{ km/h} = 10 \text{ m/s}$$
$$\therefore 32 \text{ km/h} = 10 \times \frac{32}{36}$$
$$= \textbf{8·89 m/s}$$

i.e. to change km/h to m/s, multiply by $\frac{10}{36}$.

N.B. Since m/s is always less than km/h (i.e. 36 as compared with 10) the smaller figure 10 appears on the top line.

Example 2.

A motor lorry has a mass of 1 500 kg. Find the power developed by the engine if it travels at a speed of 50 km/h against a tractive resistance of 0·06 N/kg.

$$\text{Speed of lorry} = 50 \text{ km/h}$$
$$= 50 \times \frac{10}{36} \text{ m/s}$$

i.e. in 1 second the lorry moves $50 \times \frac{10}{36}$

$$\text{Total resistance to motion} = \text{tractive resistance} \times \text{mass}$$
$$= 0·06 \times 1\,500$$
$$= \textbf{90 N}$$

$$\text{Work done/second by engine} = \text{force} \times \text{distance}$$
$$= 90 \times 50 \times \frac{10}{36}$$
$$= 1\,250 \text{ J}$$
$$\therefore \text{Power developed} = 1\,250 \text{ W}$$
$$= \textbf{1·25 kW}$$

E

Work Diagrams

Problems dealing with work may be illustrated by drawing work diagrams.

To obtain a work diagram, we plot a graph of the working force against the distance through which it moves.

Example 1.

A force of 50 N acts through a distance of 20 m. Calculate the work done and draw the work diagram (Fig. 170).

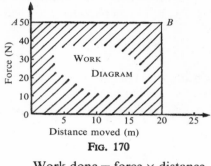

FIG. 170

Work done = force × distance
$$= 50 \times 20$$
$$= \mathbf{1\ 000\ J}$$

The distance is plotted on the horizontal scale and the force on the vertical scale. The 50 N force remains constant throughout the whole 20 m distance so that the line *AB* remains horizontal and the resulting work diagram is a rectangle.

This form of work diagram is always obtained with a constant load.

Now the length of the rectangle represents the distance moved and the height represents the working force. If we multiply the length by the height we get the area of the diagram and if we multiply the force and the distance we get the work done, so that **the area of the diagram corresponds to the work done.**

Work done by a variable force

Example

A pit cage of mass 1 000 kg is carried by a wire rope of mass 1·5 kg per metre. Find the work done in raising the cage from the bottom of a 90 m shaft. Draw the work diagram.

Mass of cage   = 1 000 kg   Mass of rope = 1·5 kg/m
Weight of cage = 9 810 N   Weight of rope = 1·5 × 9·81
                                                   = 14·7 N/m

Work done raising the cage = force × distance.
$$= 9\,810 \times 90$$
$$= 882\,900 \text{ J}$$
$$= 883 \times 10^3 \text{ J}$$

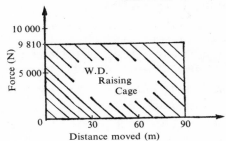

Fig. 171

Now in this case we must also consider the weight of the rope.
Total weight of the rope = 90 × 14·7
= 1 323 N

When the cage is at the bottom of the shaft, the total weight of the rope must be overcome, but, as the cage ascends, the rope is wound on the drum and the weight of the rope to be overcome decreases until the cage is at the top and there is no rope left hanging.

Thus the weight of the rope varies from 1 323 N, when the cage is at the bottom, to 0 N when the cage is at the top.

So that the average force due to the rope $= \dfrac{1\,323 + 0}{2}$
= 661·5 N

and distance moved = 90 m
Work done raising the rope = Average force × distance
$$= 661·5 \times 90$$
= 59 535 J

We may draw the work diagram and check our calculation by finding the area.

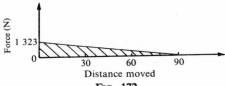

Fig. 172

124   APPLIED MECHANICS

Area of Diagram $= \frac{1}{2}$ base $\times$ altitude

$$= 0.5 \times 90 \times 1\ 323$$

$$= \textbf{59 535 units}$$

i.e. work done raising the rope $= \textbf{59.5} \times \textbf{10}^3$ **J**

N.B.—The same result could be obtained by considering the total weight
of the rope to be concentrated at its centre of gravity, i.e. at the
mid point of its length. The calculated result would be the same
but the work diagram would be a different shape.

Total work done $=$ W.D. on cage $+$ W.D. on rope

$$= 883 \times 10^3 + 59.5 \times 10^3$$

$$= \textbf{942.5} \times \textbf{10}^3 \textbf{ J}$$

Combined diagram for W.D. on both cage and rope (Fig. 173).

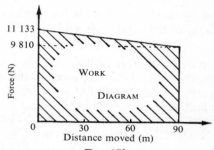

Fig. 173

Example 2.

A well (Fig. 174) is 10 m deep and contains 3 m of water. If the well
is 2 m in dia. find the work done emptying the well. 1 m³ of water
has a mass of 1 000 kg).

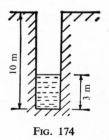

Fig. 174

Volume of water in the well $= \dfrac{\pi D^2}{4} \times 3$

$$= \dfrac{\pi \times 4}{4} \times 3$$

$$= \textbf{9·42 m}^3$$

Weight of water $= 9·42 \times 1\,000 \times 9·81$

$$= \textbf{92 410 N}$$

We may draw the work diagram (Fig. 175) and by calculating the area, find the work done.

The total weight of water must be raised through 7 m but, as the water is removed from the well, the weight of water still to be lifted decreases until at the 10 m depth the load to be lifted is nil.

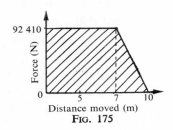

Fᴵɢ. 175

Area of work diagram $=$ area of rectangle $+$ area of triangle

$$= (92\,410 \times 7) + 0·5 \times 3 \times 92\,410)$$

$$= 646\,870 + 138\,615$$

$$= \textbf{785 485} = \textbf{785·5} \times \textbf{10}^3 \textbf{ J}$$

Alternatively we may consider the total weight of the water to be concentrated at its centre of gravity, i.e. at a point 8·5 m below ground level.

Hence

total work done raising water $=$ force $\times$ distance moved by C.G.

$$= 92\,410 \times 8·5$$

$$= \textbf{785·5} \times \textbf{10}^3 \textbf{ J}$$

Hauling

In haulage problems the load is generally on skids or on wheels and hauled by a rope or a tow-bar.

We need to know the coefficient of friction between the surface and the sliding body so that, knowing the weight of the body, we can calculate the force required to haul it using the formula $F = \mu R$. When the body is mounted on wheels, the working force is the force required to overcome tractive resistance.

Example 1.

In a dairy, metal skids are used to transfer cases of milk bottles from the bottling machine to the loading bay 20 m distant. If the skid has a mass of 10 kg and a case of milk has a mass of 5 kg find the work done sliding a skid carrying 10 cases from the machine to the bay. Co-efficient of friction between the skid and the floor = 0·10.

Total mass of skid and 10 cases = $10 + 50$

$$= \textbf{60 kg}$$

$$\text{Total weight} = 60 \times 9\cdot81 = 588\cdot6 \text{ N}$$

$$\text{Force required to move loaded skid} = \mu R$$

$$= 0\cdot1 \times 588\cdot6$$

$$= 58\cdot86 \text{ N}$$

$$\text{Work done} = \text{force} \times \text{distance}$$

$$= 58\cdot86 \times 20$$

$$= \textbf{1 177·2 N}$$

Hauling on an incline

When the body is on an incline, the same conditions apply as when it is on a horizontal surface and, in addition, the force $mg \sin \theta$ tends to slide the body down the incline (Fig. 176).

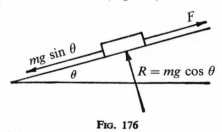

Fig. 176

There are two points here that must be watched very closely.

1. Friction and tractive resistance always oppose motion, i.e. if the body is being hauled upwards then they act down the incline, but if the body is sliding down then they act up the incline.

2. When using the friction formula $F = \mu R$, R is the perpendicular reaction between the plane and the body; i.e. $R = mg \cos \theta$. The formula now reads $F = \mu mg \cos \theta$.

Gradients

Sometimes the slope of the plane is given as, for example, "a gradient of 1 in 6." In engineering problems this is taken to denote a vertical rise of one unit for every 6 units up the sloping surface (Fig. 177) i.e. $\sin \theta = \frac{1}{6}$.

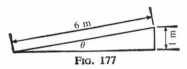

6 m

m

θ

FIG. 177

This is a very useful way of expressing the slope as it enables the force down the plane to be calculated very easily, e.g. for a slope of 1 in 6.

$$\text{force down the plane} = mg \sin \theta$$
$$= mg \times \frac{1}{6}$$
$$= \frac{mg}{6}$$

i.e. the force down the plane is one-sixth of the weight.

N.B.—In mathematics the gradient of the line is taken as the tangent of the angle, i.e. the vertical rise is compared to the horizontal distance. Engineers prefer to use the sine of the angle since it is easier to measure the slope of a hill than the horizontal distance.

Generally it does not matter very much since, when the angle θ is small, the sine is almost equal to the tangent.

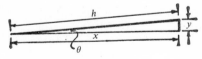

h

y

x

θ

FIG. 178

In fig. 178, x is almost equal to h.

$$\therefore \frac{y}{h} \doteqdot \frac{y}{x}$$

i.e. $\sin \theta \doteqdot \tan \theta$ if θ is a small angle.

Example

A train of 6 hutches is hauled up a gradient of 1 in 5 against a tractive resistance of 0·075 N/kg. If the speed is 6 km/h and each hutch has a mass of 600 kg find the power required by the winding engine.

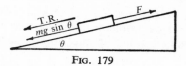

FIG. 179

Total mass of hutches $= 6 \times 600 = 3\ 600$ kg

Total tractive resistance $= 3\ 600 \times 0·075$

$$= 270 \text{ N}$$

Gravity component down the plane $= mg \sin \theta$

$$= 3\ 600 \times 9·81 \times \tfrac{1}{5}$$

$$= 7\ 063·5$$

Total force to be overcome (F) $= 7\ 063·5 \times 270$

$$= 7\ 333·5$$

Speed of hutches $= 6$ km/h

$$= 6 \times \frac{10}{36}$$

$$= 1·67 \text{ m/s}$$

Work done per second on the hutches $=$ force $\times$ distance moved/s

$$= 7\ 333 \times 1·67 = 12\ 240 \text{ J}$$

Power of winding engine $= 12\ 240$ W

$$= 12·24 \text{ kW}$$

Springs

If you open up a spring balance you will find, when you examine the working parts, that the balance measures the weight of an object by measuring the amount of extension or compression it causes in a spring.

A large load causes a large deformation (i.e. extension or compression—depending on the type of balance) of the spring while a small load causes a small deformation. You will notice further that the marks on the scale are equally spaced, showing that as successive equal forces are added the spring is deformed by equal amounts—i.e. if a force of 1 N causes it to stretch 4 mm then 2 N will cause it to stretch 8 mm and 3 N will cause a 12 mm extension. In other words, the extension or compression of the spring is proportional to the applied load. This is known as Hooke's law and we will examine it in more detail when we study engineering materials.

Stiffness of a spring

The stiffness of a spring is denoted by the force that will deform the spring by unit distance, e.g. if a force of 60 N compresses a spring by 12 mm then the stiffness of the spring is 5 N/mm. The stiffness may also be measured in N/m.

Example 1

A load of 1 000 N extends a heavy spring a distance of 0·25 m. Calculate the stiffness of the spring in N/m.

$$\text{Load on spring} = 1\ 000\ \text{N}$$
$$0\cdot25\ \text{m extension is caused by } 1\ 000\ \text{N}$$
$$1\ \text{m extension is caused by } 1\ 000 \div 0\cdot25 = 4\ 000\ \text{N}$$
$$\therefore \text{spring stiffness} = 4\ 000\ \text{N/m}$$
$$\text{i.e. spring stiffness (N/m)} = \frac{\text{force (N)}}{\text{deformation (m)}}$$

Work done compressing a spring

As a spring is compressed, the resisting force in the spring increases, so that the working force must increase as the compression increases.

In finding the work done in compression we require to take the average force exerted during the compression and the distance through which the force moves.

Example 1

The stiffness of a spring is 5 000 N/m. Find the work done in compressing the spring 0·4 m.

When the spring is not under compression the working force is zero. Since the spring stiffness is 5 000 N/m it requires a force of 5 000 N for every metre it is compressed and, since the compression is 0·4 m, the

$$\text{final force required on the spring} = 0\cdot4 \times 5\ 000$$
$$= 2\ 000\ \text{N}$$
$$\text{Average force during compression} = \frac{0 + 2\ 000}{2}$$
$$= \mathbf{1\ 000\ N}$$

Work done in compressing the spring = average force × distance

$$= 1\,000 \times 0\cdot4$$

$$= \textbf{400 J}$$

We can check by drawing the diagram for the work done on the spring and finding the area (Fig. 180).

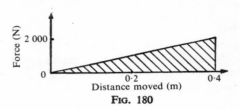

FIG. 180

Area of diagram = $\frac{1}{2}$ base × altitude

$$= 0\cdot5 \times 0\cdot4 \times 2\,000$$

$$= \textbf{400 J}$$

Examples 2.

A spring of stiffness 3 000 N/m is compressed a distance of 0·04 m. Find the work done compressing the spring another 0·05 m.

Stiffness of the spring = 3 000 N/m

When the spring is compressed 0·04 m, the force in the spring

$$= \text{Compression} \times \text{stiffness}$$

$$= 0\cdot04 \times 3\,000$$

$$= \textbf{120 N}$$

When the spring is compressed a further 0·05 m, i.e. a total of 0·09 m, force in the spring = $0\cdot09 \times 3\,000$

$$= \textbf{270 N}$$

∴ Average force used during the 0·05 compression,

$$= \frac{120 + 270}{2}$$

$$= \textbf{195 N}$$

Work done compressing the

spring = average force × distance

$$= 195 \times 0\cdot05$$

$$= \textbf{9·75 J}$$

Work done against a brake

When a brake is acting on a wheel, the wheel is moving against the friction force between the wheel and the brake lining, i.e. the wheel is doing work against the brake, and the energy given up by the wheel appears at the brake in the form of heat.

We have seen from our study of friction that if the reaction between the wheel and the brake lining is R, and the coefficient of friction is μ, the braking force on the circumference of the wheel is F N where $F = \mu R$ (Fig. 181).

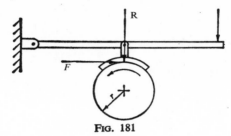

Fig. 181

If the wheel makes 1 revolution then a point on the lining moves a distance of $2\pi r$ over the surface of the wheel, where r m is the radius of the wheel.

$$\text{Work done in 1 revolution} = \text{force} \times \text{distance moved}$$
$$= \mu R \times 2\pi r \quad \text{J}$$

If the wheel rotates at n revolutions/second

$$\text{Work done per second} = \mu R \times 2\pi rn \quad \text{J}$$
$$\therefore \text{Power absorbed by the brake} = \mu R \times 2\pi rn \quad \text{W}$$
$$\text{If the friction torque} = \mu Rr$$
$$\text{Power absorbed by the brake} = 2\pi nT \quad \text{W}$$

where T is the friction torque in Nm and n is the speed of the wheel in rev/s.

Summary

$$\text{Work done against the brake in 1 revolution } = \mu R \times 2\pi r \quad \text{J}$$
$$= 2\pi T \quad \text{J}$$
$$\text{Work done against the brake in } n \text{ revolutions} = \mu R \times 2\pi rn \quad \text{J}$$
$$= 2\pi nT \quad \text{J}$$

Power absorbed $= \mu R \times 2\pi r$n　W

where $\mu =$ coefficient of friction.

$R =$ normal reaction between the wheel and brake lining in newtons

$r =$ radius of the wheel in metres

$n =$ speed of the wheel in rev/s

Example 1.

Find the power absorbed by the brake shown in Fig. 182 if the coefficient of friction between the wheel and the brake lining is 0·3 and the wheel revolves at 500 rev/min.

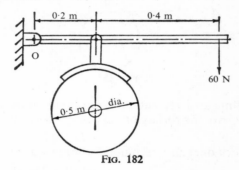

FIG. 182

Let R be the reaction between the wheel and the brake lining.

Take moments about O

$$0·2 \times R = 0·6 \times 60$$

$$\mathbf{R = 180 \ N}$$

Friction force $= F = \mu R$

$$= 0·3 \times 180$$

$$= \mathbf{54 \ N}$$

Work done in 1 revolution $= 2\pi r \times F$

$$= 2\pi \times 0·25 \times 54 \quad J$$

Work done in 1 second $= 2\pi \times 0·25 \times 54 \times \dfrac{500}{60}$

$$= 706 \ J$$

Power absorbed $= \mathbf{706 \ W}$

Work done in bearings

The action of a bearing on a shaft may be treated in the same way as that of a brake. Both brakes and bearings have a frictional resistance to the rotation of the shaft, but, whereas a brake is applied to supply a big frictional resistance, a bearing should offer as little resistance as possible.

The reaction between the shaft and the bearing is determined from the weight of the shaft plus the weight of any pulleys it may be carrying —this weight may be carried between two or more bearings. The effects of any belt drives must be considered too, for since the belts must be in tension they supply a part of the final reaction and must be taken into account.

Only the magnitude of the final reaction need be considered. It may act against the top or bottom half of the bearing; the energy absorbed will be the same.

Power lost at a bearing

The same reasonong holds for bearings as for brakes. Friction absorbs some of the energy of the shaft and this energy appears in the form of heat.

$$\text{Friction force} = \mu R$$

$$\text{Work done in 1 revolution} = \mu R \times 2\pi r$$

$$\text{Work done in } n \text{ revolutions} = \mu R \times 2\pi r n$$

$$\text{Power lost at bearing} = \mu R \times 2\pi r n$$

$$= 2\pi n T$$

Where T = friction torque in Nm

r = radius of the shaft in metres

μ = coefficient of friction between shaft and bearing

n = speed of the shaft in rev/s

Example 1.

A shaft of diameter 80 mm and mass 40 kg is mounted on two bearings 1 m apart (Fig. 183). If the shaft carries a pulley of mass 25 kg between the bearings and 0·3 m from one of them find the power lost at the nearer bearing if the shaft speed is 500 rev/min (coefficient of friction for the bearing surfaces = 0·02).

Mass of shaft = 40 kg   Mass of pulley = 25 kg
Wt of shaft   = 40 × 9·81   Wt of pulley   = 25 × 9·81
              = 392·4 N   = 245 N

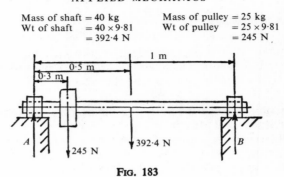

FIG. 183

Let the Reaction at Bearing B be R_b

Let the Reaction at Bearing A be R_a

Take moments about bearing A

$R_b = (0·3 \times 245) + (0·5 \times 392·4)$

$R_b = 73·5 + 196·2$

$R_b = 269·7$ N

$\therefore R_a = (392·4 + 245) - 269·7$

$= 637·4 - 269·7$

$= \mathbf{367·7\ N}$

Friction torque at Bearing $A = \mu R r$

$= 0·02 \times 367·7 \times 0·04$

$= \mathbf{0·294\ Nm}$

Power lost at Bearing $A = 2\pi n T$

$= \dfrac{2 \times 3·14 \times 500 \times 0·294}{60}$

$= \mathbf{15·4\ W}$

Belt Drives

It is not always practicable to make direct use of power developed by and engine or motor. If the power source is situated a distance from the machine it is to drive or operate, then some means of connecting the two must be employed. A simple way to do this is by means of an endless belt passing over a pulley on the driving shaft and over another pulley on the machine or **"driven"** shaft. Although not common practice today, it is possible for one driving unit to transmit power via a line of shafting and belts to several machines.

Fig. 184 shows a simple arrangement whereby power is transmitted from the **driver** to the **follower** or **driven** pulley by means of a belt.

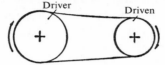

FIG. 184   OPEN BELT DRIVE

When the belt passes directly from the top of one pulley to the top of the other and from the bottom of one to the bottom of the other it is known as an *open belt drive*. It can be seen in the sketch (Fig. 184) that if the driver is rotating clockwise, then the driven will also rotate clockwise.

If the belt is now made to pass from the top of the driver to the underside of the driven and from the top of the driven to the underside of the driver, the belt will cross over on itself somewhere between the two pulleys (Fig. 185).

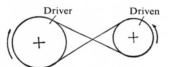

FIG. 185   CROSSED BELT DRIVE

This is known as **crossed belt drive** and it has the effect of reversing the direction of rotation between the driver and the driven. Thus, if the driver rotates clockwise, the driven rotates anticlockwise.

Belt Tensions

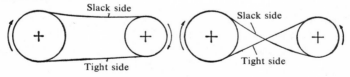

FIG. 186

When transmitting power by belts, the driving pulley is in effect pulling on one side of the belt and the belt is transferring this "pull" to the driven pulley, causing it to rotate. The other side of the belt is always slightly slacker than the driving side (Fig. 186).

We have, then, two tensions in any one belt—the tight side T_1 and the slack side T_2.

The effective force or tension in a belt will, therefore, be equal to $(T_1 - T_2)$. This tension is expressed in one of three ways:—
1. As the total effective tension in a belt, $(T_1 - T_2)$,
2. It may be given as a tension in newtons per metre width of belt,
3. T_2 may be given as a fraction of T_1. e.g. $T_1 = 2 \cdot 5\ T_2$.

All tensions are measured in newtons.

Power transmitted by a belt

Now consider a pulley of diameter D m revolving at n rev/s. (Fig. 187).

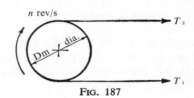

FIG. 187

Effective tension in belt $= (T_1 - T_2)$ newtons

$\therefore$ Work done in 1 revolution $=$ distance $\times$ force

$$= \pi D \times (T_1 - T_2) \quad \text{J}$$

$$\text{Work done/s} = \pi \times D \times n\ (T_1 - T_2) \quad \text{J}$$

$$\text{Power transmitted} = = \pi D n (T_1 - T_2) \quad \text{W}$$

Example

A pulley 2 m in diameter revolves at 250 rev/min. The tensions in the tight and slack sides are 350 N and 140 N respectively.

Calculate:—

     (*a*) the power transmitted assuming no slip,
     (*b*) the width of the belt if the maximum permissible tension is
        not to exceed 2 000 N/m width of belt,
     (*c*) the relationship between T_1 and T_2.

Dia. of pulley $= D = 2$ m

Speed $\qquad = n = \dfrac{250}{60}$ rev/s

Tension (tight) $= T_1 = 350$ N

Tension (slack) $= T_2 = 140$ N

(a)   Power transmitted $= \pi Dn(T_1 - T_2)$

$$= \frac{\pi \times 2 \times 250\,(350 - 140)}{60}$$

$$= \frac{\pi \times 2 \times 250 \times 210}{60}$$

$$= \textbf{5 490 W}$$

(b)   Maximum belt tension $= 350$ N
Permissible tension $= 2\,000$ N/m width

$$\therefore \text{Width of belt} = \frac{350}{2\,000}$$

$$= \textbf{0·175 m} = \textbf{175 mm}$$

(c)   Relationship between T_1 and T_2 $\dfrac{T_1}{T_2} = \dfrac{350}{140}$

$$= 2·5$$

i.e. $\dfrac{T_1}{T_2} = 2·5$

$$\therefore \quad \textbf{T}_1 = \textbf{2·5 T}_2$$

Belt slip
So far we have assumed that there will be no slipping between the belt and pulley surfaces. In practice this is not so. Owing to stretching of the belt material, and to the contact surfaces becoming polished, a small degree of slipping will take place.

The amount of slip is generally expressed as a percentage of the power transmitted.

Example
A driving pulley develops 9 kW. If there is a 3% slip, calculate the power transmitted by a belt drive from this pulley to a machine.

Power developed $= 9$ kW

Percentage slip $= 3$

This means that 3/100 of the total power is lost due to belt slip.
∴ Only 97/100 of the total power is actually received by the machine.

Power received by machine $= \dfrac{9}{1} \times \dfrac{97}{100}$

$$= \textbf{8·73 kW}$$

Belt slip will also be responsible for a loss of speed of the driven pulley. If there is no slipping, then the peripheral speed of the driven pulley must be the same as that of the driver. When slip is present, however, the peripheral speed of the driven will fall below that of the driver thus causing a drop in rev/min.

Example

It is known that a driving pulley revolving at 400 rev/min should cause a driven pulley to rotate at 150 rev/min when there is no slip.

Calculate the speed in rev/min of the driver when there is 4% slip.

$$\text{rev/min of driver} = 400$$

$$\text{Percentage slip} = 4$$

In order to maintain 150 rev/min by the driven pulley, the driver must have its speed increased.

i.e. If 4/100ths of the driver's speed is lost due to slip, then 96/100ths is actually transmitted.

$$\text{Required speed of driver} = \frac{400}{1} \times \frac{100}{96}$$

$$= \mathbf{416 \cdot 67 \ rev/min}$$

Toothed Wheels

In early times power was transmitted by rotating cylinders in close contact. This was purely a friction drive and since surface wear was excessive, much of the transmitted power was lost because of slipping.

The need for greater efficiency in power transmission has led to the development of gear teeth. The gear tooth has evolved from the friction drive to its present form over a period of several hundred years. Even so, the calculations necessary in tooth form design are still based on a circle, the circumference of which represents the circumference of a cylinder as used in a pure friction drive.

This circle is known as the **pitch circle** and its diameter, the pitch circle diameter or P.C.D., will be used in our calculations.

The circular pitch or C.P. is the distance from a point on one tooth to a corresponding point on the adjacent tooth measured along the pitch circle.

Some of the important features in the design of a gear tooth are shown in the sketch (Fig. 188).

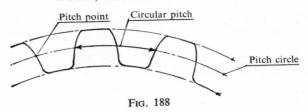

FIG. 188

When two gears are in mesh, contact between their teeth takes place on the pitch circle at the pitch point, and the circular pitch must be the same in both gears.

To calculate the pitch circle diameter

If the number of teeth in the gear is t and the circular pitch is P, then the circumference of the pitch circle $= P \times t$

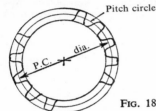

FIG. 189

and also $= \pi \times \text{P.C.D.}$

i.e. $\pi \times \text{P.C.D.} = P \times t$

$\therefore \text{P.C.D.} = \dfrac{Pt}{\pi}$

Example

Calculate the P.C.D. of a gear having 32 teeth and a C.P. of 15 mm.

$$\text{P.C.D.} = \frac{\text{C.P.} \times \text{number of teeth}}{\pi}$$

$$= \frac{15 \times 32}{\pi}$$

$$= \mathbf{152 \cdot 8} \text{ mm}$$

Now consider a tooth of a gear transmitting a force F N to a tooth in mesh with it (Fig. 190).

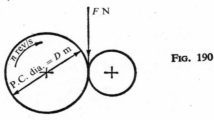

FIG. 190

Since contact between meshing gears is on the pitch circle, in one revolution work done by $F =$ distance × force

$$= \pi \times D \times F \text{ joules}$$

Work done/second $= \pi \times D \times F \times n$

Power transmitted $= \pi DFn$ W

Where $D =$ P.C. dia in metres

$\quad F =$ force in newtons

$\quad n =$ speed in rev/s

Example

Calculate the work done per second and hence the power transmitted by a spur gear with a P.C.D. of 160 mm revolving at 500 rev/min when the force transmitted by each tooth is estimated at 1 000 N.

$$\text{P.C.D.} = 160 \text{ mm}$$

$$= 0\cdot16 \text{ m}$$

$$\text{Force} = F = 1\ 000 \text{ N}$$

$$\text{Speed} = \frac{500}{60} \text{ rev/s}$$

Work done per second $= \pi \times D \times F \times n$

$$= \pi \times 0\cdot16 \times 1\ 000 \times \frac{500}{60}$$

$$= \frac{80\pi \times 10^3}{60} \text{ J}$$

$$= \textbf{4 185 J}$$

$\therefore$ Power transmitted $= 4\ 185$ W

$$= \textbf{4}\cdot\textbf{185 kW}$$

EXERCISES

1. Find the amount of work done when a force of 15 N acts through a distance of 9 metres.
2. If it requires a force of 100 N to pull a roller across a field, find the work done in pulling it 50 metres.
3. A bag of flour has a mass of 50 kg. Find the work done in raising it to a bakery loft 15 metres above ground.

4. How much work is done in raising a steel bucket of mass 250 kg carrying 500 kg of ore to the top of a furnace 25 m high?

5. Find the total work done in dragging a box of mass 25 kg for a distance of 6 m and carrying it up a stair 4 m high if the coefficient of friction between the box and the floor is 0·25.

6. A 1 kW pump is available to raise water from an underground reservoir 10 m below ground level. Find the volume of water that could be raised per min. (1 m^3 of water has a mass of 1 000 kg).

7. In digging a bridge foundation water soaks into the workings and gathers in a sump at a rate of 300 litres per minute. Find the power of the pump required to keep the foundation dry if the water has to be raised to a height of 15 metres.

8. If a 5 tonne load has to be raised from the bottom of a pit shaft 300 metres deep in 4 minutes, find the power of the winding engine.

9. If a motor lorry of mass 2·5 tonnes travels at 30 km/h against a tractive resistance of 60 N/tonne, find the power developed by the engine.

10. A railway engine of mass 70 tonnes draws a train of 8 coaches each of mass 20 tonnes against a tractive resistance of 90 N/tonne. If the engine develops 414 kW, find the speed at which it travels.

11. A car engine develops 1·9 kW as it drives the car, of mass 1 200 kg, along a road at 60 km/h. Find the tractive resistance to the motion of the car.

12. A pit hutch is drawn up a gradient of 1 in 6 at a speed of 8 km/h against a tractive resistance of 110 N/tonne. If the hutch and load has a mass of 1 500 kg find the power of the winding engine.

13. The slide valve of a steam engine is shown in Fig. 191. The slide has an area of 900 mm^2 and the pressure of the steam acting on it is $0·84 \times 10^6$ N/m^2. If the coefficient of friction between the slide and the guides is 0·04 find the power lost in friction when the driving wheel rotates at 800 rev/min.

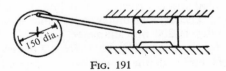

FIG. 191

14. A car of mass 900 kg developing 1·6 kW travels at a speed of 32 km/h on a level road. If the car comes to an incline of 1 in 20 find the power necessary to maintain the same speed.

15. A car of mass 950 kg travels up an incline of 1 in 24 at a speed of 40 km/h against a tractive resistance of 80 N/tonne. Find the power developed by the engine.

16. In the cylinder of an internal-combustion engine the average pressure of the gas during the working stroke is 0.56 N/mm^2. If the length of the stroke is 200 mm and the piston diameter is 120 mm, find the work done during one working stroke.

17. A well is 1.5 m in diameter and 12 m deep. If there is 3 m of water in the bottom of the well, draw the work diagram and find the amount of work done in emptying the well.

18. Draw the work diagram and calculate the work done in raising an anchor of mass 0.5 tonne from the sea bed (depth 30 m) to the deck of a ship 5 m above sea level if the anchor chain has a mass of 21 kg/m. (Neglect the water upthrust on the anchor and chain.)

19. A pit cage and its load has a mass of 4 tonnes. If the rope has a mass of 6 kg/m and the winding engine has a capacity of 35 kW, find the time it will take to raise the cage from the bottom of an 80 m shaft. Draw the work diagram.

20. A chain has a mass of 9 kg/m. Find the work done winding 100 m of the chain up an incline of 1 in 6 if the tractive resistance is 1 600 N/tonne. Draw the work diagram.

21. A strong steel spring has a stiffness of 5 N/mm. Draw the work diagram and find the amount of work done in compressing the spring 150 mm.

22. A spring of stiffness 0.4 N/mm is under a 50 mm compression. Draw the work diagram and find the work done in compressing it a further 130 mm.

23. A valve spring in a motor car is under a 10 mm compression when the valve is closed. When the valve is fully open the spring is compressed a further 5 mm. Find the power lost at the valve spring if the valve opens 1 200 times per minute and the stiffness of the spring is 0.4 N/mm.

24. A drilling machine is driven from a line of shafting running at 160 rev/min. The driving pulley is 450 mm in diameter and the machine pulley is 200 mm diameter. Calculate the speed of the machine is (a) there is no slip, (b) there is 3 per cent slip.

25. A pulley, 600 mm in diameter, drives a second pulley by means of a belt. The belt tensions are 920 N and 360 N and the speed of the driving pulley is 400 rev/min. What power is being transmitted by the belt? If the maximum allowable tension in the belt must not exceed 8 N/mm width of belt, calculate the width of belt required.

26. In a belt drive the tension in the tight side of the belt is 2·5 times the tension in the slack side. The driving pulley, 700 mm in diameter, revolves at 2 000 rev/min and the belt transmits 120 kW. What are the two tensions in the belt?

27. If the belt used in question 26 is 9 mm thick, and the maximum tension must not exceed 3 N/mm^2 of cross section, find the width of belt necessary.

28. If a gear wheel has 180 teeth and a P.C.D. of 1 204 mm, calculate the circular pitch.

29. A spur gear is transmitting 20 kW when revolving at 300 rev/min. If the P.C.D. is 250 mm, calculate the force set up in the contact tooth.

30. What power is transmitted by a gear-wheel revolving at 250 rev/min if it has 80 teeth and a C.P. of 7 mm. The estimated load on the contact tooth is 2 000 N.

CHAPTER VII

MACHINES

The word "Machine" conjures up all sorts of mental pictures of railway locomotives, turbo-jet engines, Diesel and Petrol engines and the like.

True, these are all machines, but in a very complicated form. In our study of machines we are going to confine ourselves to some of the more basic forms of the machine like pulley systems, the screw jack and gear trains.

Let us begin our investigation of machines by carrying out four simple experiments involving pulleys.

The apparatus required is two pulley blocks each having two pulleys, a length of cord or rope to suit the grooves of the pulleys and a suitable selection of masses.

Experiment No. 1

Arrange the pulleys as shown in Fig. 192.

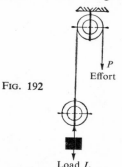

FIG. 192

P
Effort

Load L

One end of the rope is attached to the lower block and the other end passes over one pulley in the upper block. A known mass, say 5 kg, is now attached to the lower block. The total mass now supported at L will be equal to the known mass + the mass of the lower block. If this block has a mass of 2 kg then the total mass at $L = 7$ kg.

i.e. Load L (N) $= (7 \times 9.81)$
$= 68.67$ N

144

To the free end of the rope, attach **a sufficient mass at** P to balance the mass at L. When the correct mass is established, it will be found that a small increase in the mass at P causes the mass at L to rise and a small decrease causes it to fall.

For the purpose of this investigation, we will record the effort which will just cause the load to rise.

We also notice that if we make the mass at L move through a given distance, say 200 mm, the effort also moves through a distance of 200 mm. This fact is also recorded.

Experiments 2, 3 and 4

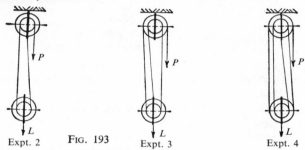

Expt. 2   FIG. 193   Expt. 3   Expt. 4

Experiments 2, 3 and 4 (Fig. 193) are carried out in the same way as experiment 1. The load remains the same in each case and the effort is adjusted as required. When the correct effort has been found, the load is moved through a definite distance, say 200 mm, and the corresponding distance moved by the effort is measured.

Results

The results of the four experiments are shown in tabular form.

Expt. No.	Total mass at L (kg)	Total Load (N)	Total mass at P (kg)	Effort (N)	Distance moved by Effort (mm)	Distance moved by Load (mm)
1	10	98·1			200	200
2	10	98·1			400	200
3	10	98·1			600	200
4	10	98·1			800	200

Throughout the investigation, care has been taken to keep the total load and the distance through which it moves, constant.

If we examine the results, we find that we can decrease the magnitude of the effort if we increase the distance through which it moves. This has been achieved by altering the design of the machine. Generally speaking, the smaller the effort required to overcome a given load, the more advantage we get from using a machine.

This advantage is known as the **mechanical advantage** of the machine and is expressed as the ratio of the load/effort.

$$\text{i.e. } \textbf{Mechanical Advantage} = \frac{\textbf{Load (N)}}{\textbf{Effort (N)}}$$

The load and effort must be measured in the same units, i.e. newtons. Mechanical advantage, therefore, has no units.

We can make a similar comparison of the distances moved by the effort and the load. The results show that, as the design of the machine is altered, so also is the distance through which the effort moves. The ratio of the distance moved by the effort to the distance moved by the load is termed the **velocity ratio.**

$$\text{i.e. } \textbf{Velocity Ratio} = \frac{\textbf{Distance moved by effort (m)}}{\textbf{Distance moved by load (m)}}$$

It should be remembered that, in any one machine, the velocity ratio is constant. In other words, the velocity ratio cannot be altered without altering the design of the machine.

The term velocity is usually associated with speed; e.g. moving through a distance of 45 kilometres in 1 hour (45 km/h) or moving through a distance of 1 metre in 1 second (1 m/s).

The velocity ratio of a machine may be calculated by using the ratio of distances only, because we assume that both the load and the effort move together for the same duration of time and so, in the calculation, the time factor will cancel, leaving a ratio of distances only.

The results show that a relatively small effort could be made to produce enough energy to overcome a much greater load. The machine, in this case the pulleys, must, therefore, convert the energy produced by the effort into a form suitable to overcome the load. This conversion forms the basis of all machines.

A machine is a device designed for the purpose of taking in some definite form of energy, modifying it, and delivering it in a form more suitable for the desired purpose.

Example 1

Calculate the mechanical advantage of a machine which raises a mass of 114 kg. The effort required is 80 N.

$$\begin{aligned}
\text{Mechanical advantage} &= \frac{\text{load}}{\text{effort}} \\
&= \frac{(114 \times 9\cdot81)}{80} \\
&= \textbf{14}
\end{aligned}$$

Example 2

During a test on a machine it was found that a 200 mm movement of the effort displaced the load by an amount equal to 15 mm. Calculate the velocity ratio of this machine.

$$\text{Velocity ratio} = \frac{\text{distance moved by effort}}{\text{distance moved by load}}$$

$$= \frac{200}{15}$$

$$= \mathbf{13 \cdot 3}$$

Example 3

The velocity ratio of a heavy lifting machine is given as 16. If it is known that the load is raised through a distance of 150 mm, calculate the corresponding distance moved by the effort.

$$\text{Velocity ratio} = \frac{\text{distance moved by effort}}{\text{distance moved by load}}$$

$$\therefore \text{Distance moved by effort} = \text{distance moved by load} \times \text{velocity ratio}$$

$$= 150 \times 6$$

$$= 2\,400 \text{ mm}$$

$$= \mathbf{2 \cdot 4 \text{ m}}$$

Efficiency

It will be remembered that in our earlier work on friction we found that, before a body can move, the force of friction must be overcome. In all machines this friction force is always present—in the bearings, between gear teeth, between sliding surfaces, etc.—and it absorbs some of the work put into the machine by the effort.

The extra work necessary to overcome the frictional resistances can be obtained only by increasing the effort since the distance through which it moves cannot be altered without altering the machine mechanism.

Because of these frictional losses the amount of work put into a machine is greater than the amount of work got out.

A comparison of the work got out and the work put into a machine gives an indication of its **efficiency** and it is often expressed as a percentage.

The efficiency of a machine is the ratio of the work got out to the work put in.

$$\textbf{Efficiency} = \frac{\textbf{Work got out of the machine (J)}}{\textbf{Work put into the machine (J)}}$$

Now let us suppose that no work is lost due to friction, etc.; then the work put into the machine = work got out of the machine.

$$\text{Efficiency} = \frac{\text{work got out of the machine}}{\text{work put into the machine}}$$

$$= \frac{1}{1}$$

$$= 1$$

$$\text{or} = 100\%$$

When this is assumed, the machine is termed an **ideal machine.** Owing mainly to the effect of friction, however, this is purely a theoretical machine and does not exist in practice.

Although we have stated that the efficiency of a machine is the ratio of the work got out to the work put in, it can be shown that:—

M.A./V.R. = efficiency

Work put in = effort × distance moved by effort

Work got out = load × distance moved by load

$$\text{Efficiency} = \frac{\text{work got out}}{\text{work put in}} = \frac{\text{load} \times \text{distance moved by load}}{\text{effort} \times \text{distance moved by effort}}$$

But $\dfrac{\text{load}}{\text{effort}} = \text{M.A.}$ and $\dfrac{\text{distance moved by load}}{\text{distance moved by effort}} = \dfrac{1}{\text{V.R.}}$

$$\text{Efficiency} = \frac{\text{M.A.}}{1} \times \frac{1}{\text{V.R.}}$$

$$= \frac{\text{M.A.}}{\text{V.R.}}$$

This is **not** a definition of efficiency.

Example

During the test on a simple machine, the following results were obtained:—

Effort = 60 N   Distance moved by effort = 1 m

Mass of load = 30 kg   Distance moved by load = 0·15 m

Calculate the M.A., V.R. and the efficiency of the machine.

$$\text{Mechanical advantage} = \frac{\text{load}}{\text{effort}}$$

$$= \frac{30 \times 9 \cdot 81}{60}$$

$$= 4 \cdot 9$$

$$\text{Velocity ratio} = \frac{\text{distance moved by effort}}{\text{distance moved by load}}$$

$$= \frac{1}{0 \cdot 15}$$

$$\text{Efficiency} = \frac{\text{work got out}}{\text{work put in}}$$

$$= \frac{30 \times 9 \cdot 81 \times 0 \cdot 15}{60 \times 1}$$

$$= 0 \cdot 735$$

Or, when expressed as a percentage,

$$\text{Efficiency} = 0 \cdot 735 \times 100$$

$$= 73 \cdot 5 \%$$

The ideal machine

It has already been stated that the efficiency of an ideal machine is 100% or 1, and that the efficiency in general was equal to the ratio M.A./V.R.

$$\therefore \text{M.A./V.R.} = 1$$

$$\therefore \text{M.A.} = \text{V.R. (for ideal machine only)}$$

Example

In an ideal machine with a velocity ratio of 8, the mass of the load to be raised is 20 kg. Calculate the effort required.

Since the machine is ideal

$$\text{M.A.} = \text{V.R.}$$

$$\therefore \text{M.A.} = 8$$

$$\text{But M.A.} = \frac{\text{load}}{\text{effort}}$$

$$\text{Effort} = \frac{\text{load}}{\text{M.A.}}$$

$$= \frac{20 \times 9 \cdot 81}{8}$$

$$= 24 \cdot 5 \text{ N}$$

i.e. **Effort required = 24·5 N**

Pulley Systems

A pulley is an adaption of the wheel. When used to transmit power, the periphery is shaped to suit the form of transmission used.

e.g. with a flat belt transmission the pulley is slightly cambered;
     with a "Vee" belt transmission the pulley has a Vee groove;
     with a chain belt transmission the pulley is toothed or it can have a series of recesses into which the chain links fit.

These examples are shown in the following sketches (Fig. 194).

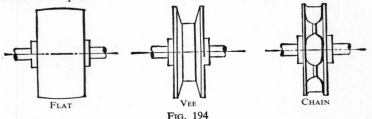

FLAT   VEE   CHAIN

FIG. 194

Now, we will investigate some of the more common pulley arrangements.

Single pulley

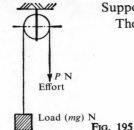

FIG. 195

Suppose the load mg (Fig. 195) is raised by 200 mm. The effort P is lowered by 200 mm.

$$V.R. = \frac{\text{distance moved by effort}}{\text{distance moved by load}}$$

$$= \frac{200}{200}$$

$$= 1$$

Two pulleys

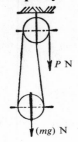

FIG. 196

Suppose the load mg (Fig. 196) is raised by 200 mm, the supporting ropes *each* shorten by 200 mm. The effort P is lowered by 400 mm.

$$V.R. = \frac{\text{distance moved by effort}}{\text{distance moved by load}}$$

$$= \frac{400}{200}$$

$$= 2$$

Three pulleys

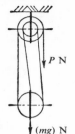

P N

(*mg*) N

FIG. 197

Suppose the load *mg* (Fig. 197) is raised by 200 mm, the supporting ropes *each* shorten by 200 mm. The effort *P* is lowered by 600 mm.

$$\text{V.R.} = \frac{\text{distance moved by effort}}{\text{distance moved by load}}$$

$$= \frac{600}{200}$$

$$= 3$$

Four pulleys

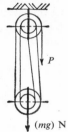

P

(*mg*) N

FIG. 198

Suppose the load *mg* (Fig. 198) is raised by 200 mm, the supporting ropes *each* shorten by 200 mm. The effort *P* is lowered by 800 mm.

$$\text{V.R.} = \frac{\text{distance moved by effort}}{\text{distance moved by load}}$$

$$= \frac{800}{200}$$

$$= 4$$

By this time it will be apparent that, for the arrangements shown, the velocity ratio is the same as the number of ropes supporting the load. This rule holds for all similar pulley arrangements.

Terms associated with pulley systems

Pulley:—a grooved wheel free to revolve on a spindle.

Block:—the frame which houses the pulley or pulleys.

Sheaves:—a number of pulleys mounted in a block.

Falls:—the ropes supporting the load.

Block and tackle:—the components of the lifting device as a whole.

Snatch block:—a single pulley, the block of which supports the load.

The snatch block

The snatch block is a convenient means of attaching the load to a looped or endless rope.

It consists of a pulley mounted in a frame carrying a hook or shackle. Fig. 199 shows a snatch block in use. If 200 mm of rope is pulled through

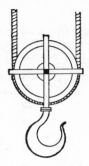

FIG. 199

the block, 100 mm will come from each side and the load will. therefore, rise a distance of 100 mm—i.e. the block will be raised or lowered by *half* the amount of rope passed through the block.

Note—The rope passing through the snatch block should be as near parallel as possible.

Gearing and Gear Trains

When the teeth of one gear-wheel fit exactly into the spaces of another, then the gears are said to be in **mesh.**

Consider two gears in mesh (Fig. 200). When gear A rotates in a clockwise direction, it will cause gear B to rotate in an anti-clockwise direction. The inclusion of a third gear, C (Fig. 201), changes the direction of rotation of gear B so that gears A and B now rotate in the same direction.

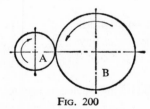

FIG. 200

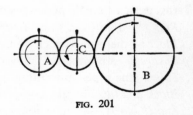

FIG. 201

It is found that an **even** number of gears in mesh cause the last gear in the series to rotate in the opposite direction to that of the first, while an **odd** number of gears cause the first and last gears to rotate in the same direction.

When two or more gear wheels are in mesh, the resulting arrangement is known as a **train of gears.**

Suppose the two wheels shown in Fig. 202 are in mesh; wheel *A* has 50 teeth and wheel *B* has 100 teeth.

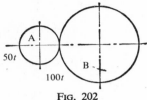

FIG. 202

If wheel *A* makes one complete revolution, then its 50 teeth will have passed 50 teeth of wheel *B*, leaving a further 50 still to pass. Thus it will take one more revolution—two in all—of wheel *A* to pass all 100 teeth of wheel *B*.

The speed in rev/min of wheel *A* must, therefore, be twice that of wheel *B*. For example:—

If wheel *A* revolves at 200 rev/min, wheel *B* revolves at 100 rev/min.

If wheel *B* revolves at 350 rev/min, wheel *A* revolves at 700 rev/min.

Although wheel *A* and wheel *B* are turning at different speeds, they are in constant mesh and, therefore, turning during the same interval of time.

When wheel *A* is driving wheel *B*, the velocity ratio is given by:—

$$\text{V.R.} = \frac{\textbf{speed of wheel A}}{\textbf{speed of wheel B}}$$

Now let us consider the two gear-wheels *A* and *B* (Fig. 203) in mesh.

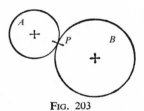

FIG. 203

Let gear *A* have *t* teeth and be turning at *r* rev/min, and let gear *B* have *T* teeth and be turning at *R* rev/min.

When *A* has turned through *r* revolutions, *rt* teeth have passed the pitch point *P* (the point of contact between the gears when in mesh) and *RT* teeth on wheel *B* engage with these.

F

Because the two gears are in mesh, $rt = RT$.

$$\frac{r}{R} = \frac{T}{t}$$

i.e. $\dfrac{\text{Speed of } A}{\text{Speed of } B} = \dfrac{\text{number of teeth on } B}{\text{number of teeth on } A}$

but velocity ratio $= \dfrac{\text{speed of } A}{\text{speed of } B}$

$\therefore$ Velocity ratio $= \dfrac{\text{number of teeth on } B}{\text{number of teeth on } A}$

In this case we assumed that wheel A was driving wheel B. Therefore, we can now state the velocity ratio as being:—

$$\textbf{V.R.} = \frac{\textbf{the number of teeth on the driven gear}}{\textbf{the number of teeth on the driving gear}}$$

Example

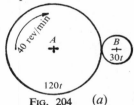

120*t*

Fig. 204

Calculate the velocity ratio of the simple gear train shown in Fig. 204,

    (*a*) by comparison of speeds,

    (*b*) by comparison of gear teeth.

(*a*)   In one rev. of A

B makes $\dfrac{120}{30}$ rev.

$\therefore$ speed of $B = \dfrac{120}{30} \times 40$

$= \textbf{160 rev/min}$

$\text{V.R.} = \dfrac{\text{speed of driver}}{\text{speed of driven}}$

$= \dfrac{40}{160}$

$= \tfrac{1}{4}$

(*b*) $\text{V.R.} = \dfrac{\text{number of teeth in driven}}{\text{number of teeth in driver}}$

$= \dfrac{30}{120}$

$= \tfrac{1}{4}$

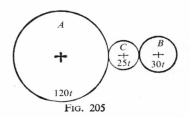

FIG. 205

Now let us suppose a third wheel, C, is inserted in mesh between wheels A and B (Fig. 205). Consider one revolution of wheel A. In the same time wheel C will make 120/25 rev., and wheel B will make 120/25 × 25/30 rev.

= 4 revs.

$$\therefore \text{Velocity ratio} = \frac{1}{4} \left[\frac{\text{speed of driver}}{\text{speed of driven}}\right]$$

This shows that, when we add an intermediate wheel to the train, the velocity ratio remains the same, but the driver (wheel A) and the driven (wheel B) now rotate in the same direction.

No matter how many wheels are in mesh in such a gear train, only the direction of the first and last wheels will vary—the velocity ratio will be constant.

The intermediate gears are often referred to as **idlers** and the arrangement as a whole is classed as a **simple train.**

Examples

Calculate the velocity ratio of each of the simple gear trains shown (Fig. 206) and mark the direction of rotation of the first and last wheels.

Note—In all cases wheel x is the driver (rotating clockwise), and wheel y the driven.

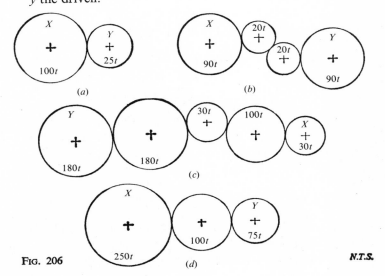

FIG. 206   N.T.S.

Compound gear trains

Another arrangement of gears is as follows (Fig. 207):—

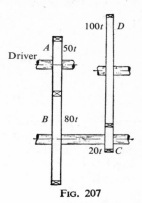

FIG. 207

Here wheels B and C are fixed or *keyed* to the same shaft.

Therefore, if wheel B makes one revolution, wheel C must also make one revolution.

Now consider one revolution of wheel A.

   wheel B makes 50/80 rev.

   wheel C makes 50/80 rev.

   wheel D makes $50/80 \times 20/100$ rev.

$$= \frac{1}{8} \text{ rev.}$$

Velocity ratio $= \dfrac{\text{speed of driver}}{\text{speed of driven—i.e. the final driven}}$
               gear (gear D)

$$= \frac{1}{\frac{1}{8}}$$

$$= 8$$

This type of arrangement, made up of two or more simple trains, is known as a **compound gear train.**

As the sketches show, the difference between a simple gear train and a compound gear train lies in the way the gears are arranged to produce the final drive.

In a simple train **all** the gears are in direct mesh, while in a compound train two or more simple trains are coupled together by a common shaft.

Example

Calculate the velocity ratio of the following compound gear train (Fig. 208):—

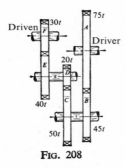

FIG. 208

$$\text{V.R.} = \frac{\text{speed of driver}}{\text{speed of driven}}$$

Consider 1 rev. of A

B makes $\dfrac{75}{45}$ rev.

D makes $\dfrac{75}{45} \times \dfrac{50}{20}$ rev.

E makes $\dfrac{75}{45} \times \dfrac{50}{20}$ rev.

F makes $\dfrac{75}{45} \times \dfrac{50}{20} \times \dfrac{40}{30} = 5\cdot55$ rev.

$$\therefore \text{V.R.} = \frac{1}{5\cdot55}$$

Note—When the gear train consists of more than two gears, the velocity ratio is given by the product of the numbers of teeth on the driven gears, divided by the product of the numbers of teeth on the drivers.

$$\text{Velocity ratio} = \frac{\textbf{product of teeth on driven gears}}{\textbf{product of teeth on drivers}}$$

The initial drive to a gear train is often supplied by a power unit whose speed range is limited—electric motor, petrol or diesel engine, etc.

Without some means of modifying the speed of the initial drive, then, for any particular output speed, a special driving motor would have to be designed.

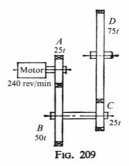

FIG. 209

In Fig. 209 we have an electric motor developing 240 revolutions per minute (rev/min) and it is necessary to know how many rev/min are available at the wheel D.

Consider 1 rev. of wheel A,

$$\text{then wheel } B \text{ makes } \frac{25}{50} \text{ rev.}$$

$$\text{wheel } C \text{ makes } \frac{25}{50} \text{ rev.}$$

$$\text{and wheel } D \text{ makes } \frac{25}{50} \times \frac{25}{75} \text{ rev.}$$

But since wheel A actually makes 240 rev/min,

$$\text{then wheel } D \text{ makes } \frac{25}{50} \times \frac{25}{75} \times 240 \text{ rev/min}$$

$$= \textbf{40 rev/min.}$$

Gearing which causes a drop in speed like this is called **reduction gearing**.

Now with the same electric motor but the gears changed (Fig. 210) we will again find how many rev/min are available at wheel D.

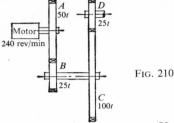

Fig. 210

Consider 1 rev. of wheel A, then wheel B makes $\frac{50}{25}$ rev.

wheel C makes $\frac{50}{25}$ rev.

and wheel D makes $\frac{50}{25} \times \frac{100}{25}$ rev.

But since wheel A is making 240 rev/min,

wheel D develops $\frac{50}{25} \times \frac{100}{25} \times 240$

$$= \mathbf{1920 \ rev/min.}$$

By altering the size of the gears in the train, we can have an almost limitless number of output speeds from a constant speed initial drive. In order that these variations might be effected, it would be necessary to stop the machine, dismantle the existing gear train, rearrange and reassemble. This could take a considerable time and cause much inconvenience.

To obviate this wastage of time and labour, the gear box has been developed. By this arrangement, a constant speed motor can be made to give a variety of prearranged speeds.

A gear box is a unit in which is housed a compound gear train which

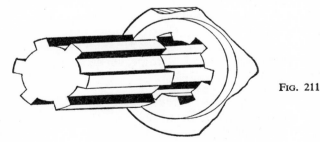

Fig. 211

can be altered by the engagement of alternative gear wheels. Two or more gears of different sizes are fixed together to form a **cluster.** The cluster has slots cut on the shaft bore (Fig. 211) leaving a serrated hole. The shaft also has axial slots so that, when the cluster and the shaft are assembled, the serrations of the cluster fit into the slots of the shaft. The gears can now slide axially on the shaft but, when the shaft rotates, the gears must also rotate. This slotting is known as **splining.**

In Fig. 212 gears A and D are fixed together and, as a cluster, operate on a splined shaft. The final drive is taken from this shaft. Gears B and

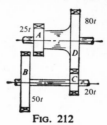

FIG. 212

C are fixed or keyed to a second shaft, this shaft producing the initial drive at 200 rev/min.

1. With gears C and D engaged, consider 1 rev. of C,

$$\text{then } D \text{ makes } \frac{20}{80} \text{ rev.}$$

$$\text{and speed of } D = \frac{20}{80} \times 200$$

$$= \textbf{50 rev/min.}$$

2. With gears B and A engaged, consider 1 rev. of B,

$$\text{then } A \text{ makes } \frac{50}{25} \text{ rev.}$$

$$\text{and speed of } A = \frac{50}{25} \times 200$$

$$= \textbf{400 rev/min.}$$

By the insertion of more gears, a greater number of input-output ratios can be obtained.

Reverse Gear

We have already seen that the introduction of an extra gear changes the direction of the **final** rotation.

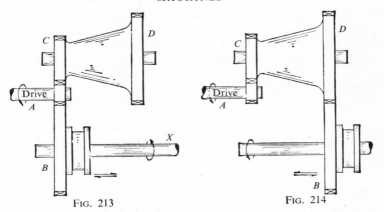

FIG. 213   FIG. 214

Referring to Fig. 213, if the initial drive through *A* is anticlockwise, the normal final drive at *X* will be clockwise, with the cluster *C-D* idling.

Gear *B* is moved along the splined shaft to mesh with gear *D*. The initial drive is now transmitted to gear *B* through the cluster *C-D* (Fig. 214). The final drive at *B* now rotates in the same direction as the initial drive.

Summary

Gears *A* and *B* in mesh

Drive	.	.	.	.	Anticlockwise
Output	.	.	.	.	Clockwise

Gears *A* and *C* in mesh and *D* and *B* in mesh

Drive	.	.	.	.	Anticlockwise
Output	.	.	.	.	Anticlockwise

Rack and Pinion

This mechanism consists of a toothed wheel, the pinion, in mesh with teeth cut in a length of straight material, the rack (Fig. 215).

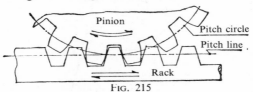

FIG. 215

The pitch circle of the rack is considered to be a circle of infinite radius so that it becomes a straight line, and because of this it is called the **pitch line.**

The sides or flanks of its teeth are straight and not curved as they are in ordinary gear teeth. Contact between the teeth of the rack and the pinion takes place on the pitch line and the pitch circle respectively and if the teeth are in mesh both rack and pinion must have the same pitch.

If the axis of the pinion is fixed, then in one revolution the rack will move a distance equal to the pitch circle circumference of the pinion.

Example 1

Calculate the distance moved by a rack when its pinion has a pitch-circle circumference of 400 mm and it makes 4 revolutions.

Distance moved by rack $= 400 \times 4 = 1\ 600$ mm

Example 2

A pinion has a circular pitch of 12 mm and 60 teeth. How far will.it move its rack in 5 revolutions?

Pitch-circle circumference $= (12 \times 60) = 720$ mm

Distance moved by rack in 5 revs $= (720 \times 5) = 3\ 600$ mm

Practical Machines

The screw jack

The principle of the screw jack is that of a nut on a screw. The nut is incorporated in the body of the jack and as the screw is rotated in one direction it will rise and in the opposite direction it will fall.

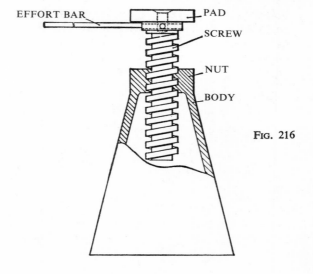

EFFORT BAR

PAD

SCREW

NUT

BODY

Fig. 216

The screw of the jack is usually based on a right hand square thread form and the screw passes into a nut, which is an integral part of the body.

The free end is covered by a pad free to rotate about the axis of the screw and designed to carry the load. Rotation of the screw is achieved by means of a bar inserted in a hole at the top of the screw (Fig. 216).

If the screw makes one complete revolution, one full thread is passed through the nut. Thus, after one clockwise revolution of the screw, point A would be in the position A_1. This displacement is equivalent to the pitch of the screw thread which, like the pitch of gear teeth, **is the distance from a point on one thread form to a corresponding point on the next adjacent thread form (Fig. 217).**

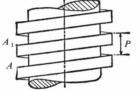

Fig. 217

If a screw has a pitch of 6 mm, then the actual distance moved in one revolution will be 6 mm.

In one revolution then, the load on top of the screw will move a distance equal to the pitch of the screw, and the effort will move a distance equal to $2\pi R$ where R is the distance from the centre of the screw to the point of application of the effort.

$$\text{Velocity ratio} = \frac{\text{distance moved by effort}}{\text{distance moved by load}}$$

$$= \frac{2\pi R}{\text{pitch}}$$

Example

Calculate the velocity ratio of a screw jack which has an effective pitch of 6 mm and the effort acting at a radius of 250 mm.

$$\text{Effort radius} = R = 250 \text{ mm}$$

$$\text{Pitch} = P = 6 \text{ mm}$$

$$\text{Velocity ratio} = \frac{\text{distance moved by effort}}{\text{distance moved by load}}$$

$$= \frac{2\pi R}{P}$$

$$= \frac{2 \times \pi \times 250}{6}$$

$$= \mathbf{261 \cdot 7}$$

Example 2

Find the effective length of effort "arm" supplied with a screw jack whose V.R. is known to be 160 and the pitch of the screw is 3 mm.

$$\text{Velocity ratio} = 160$$

$$\text{Pitch} = P = 3 \text{ mm}$$

$$\text{V.R.} = \frac{\text{distance moved by effort}}{\text{distance moved by load}}$$

$$= \frac{2\pi R}{3}$$

$$\therefore 2\pi R = 3 \times 160$$

$$\therefore \quad R = \frac{160 \times 3}{2\pi}$$

$$= \mathbf{76 \cdot 4 \text{ mm}}$$

The simple wheel and axle

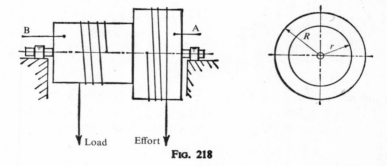

Fig. 218

An adaption of this machine is a simple windlass as used in raising a bucket from a well.

In the experimental machine the effort is supplied by the weight of a mass suspended from a cord wound round the wheel A. As the effort cord is wound off the wheel, the load cord, attached to the axle B, is wound on thus overcoming the load (Fig. 218).

Let the radius of the wheel $= R$ mm

and the radius of the axle $= r$ mm

Consider one turn of the effort wheel A, the amount of cord wound off the wheel (representing the distance moved by the effort) is equal to the circumference of A.

$$= 2\pi R$$

$$\text{Velocity ratio} = \frac{\text{distance moved by effort}}{\text{distance moved by load}} = \frac{2\pi R}{2\pi r}$$

$$= \frac{R}{r}$$

$$= \frac{\text{radius of wheel}}{\text{radius of axle}}$$

Example

Calculate the velocity ratio of an experimental wheel and axle; the wheel radius measures 400 mm and the axle radius 80 mm.

$$\text{Velocity ratio} = \frac{\text{distance moved by effort}}{\text{distance moved by load}}$$

$$= \frac{400}{80}$$

$$= \mathbf{5}$$

The wheel and differential axle

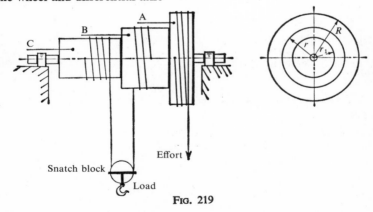

Fɪɢ. 219

A second axle C is added to the simple wheel and axle. A cord is attached and wound on axle B. After passing through a snatch block, it is given a few turns round axle C in the opposite direction to that of B, and made fast.

As the cord is wound off axle B it is wound on axle C and vice versa, when the machine rotates (Fig. 219).

> Let the radius of the effort wheel $A = R$ mm
> the radius of the large axle $B = r$ mm
> and the radius of the small axle $C = r_1$ mm

Consider one revolution of the effort wheel A.

Then the amount of cord wound off $= 2\pi R$ mm

Amount of cord wound on axle $B = 2\pi r$ mm

But at the same time some cord is wound off axle C.

Amount of cord wound off axle $C = 2\pi r_1$ mm

Effective decrease in loop length $= (2\pi r - 2\pi r_1)$ mm
$$= 2\pi(r - r_1)\text{ mm}$$

Because of the snatch block the load is raised by only half this amount,

$$\text{i.e.} \frac{2\pi(r - r_1)}{2}$$

$$\text{Velocity ratio} = \frac{\text{distance moved by effort}}{\text{distance moved by load}}$$

$$= \frac{2\pi R}{\frac{2\pi(r - r_1)}{2}}$$

$$= \frac{2R}{(r - r_1)}$$

or when diameters are used instead of radii.

$$\text{Velocity ratio} = \frac{2D}{(d - d_1)}$$

The Weston Differential Block and Tackle

This machine is a practical application of the wheel and differential axle (Fig. 220).

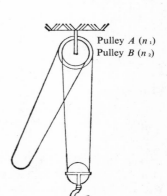

Pulley A (n_1)
Pulley B (n_2)

Fig. 220

Instead of a cord an endless chain is used and the links fit into recesses cast in the pulleys to prevent slip. The number of recesses in any one pulley is proportional to its circumference and can, therefore, be used in place of the radius when calculating the velocity ratio.

The snatch block pulley is a plain grooved pulley.

Let the number of recesses in the larger pulley $= n_1$, and

the number of recesses in the smaller pulley $= n_2$.

Consider one turn of pulley A.

Distance moved by effort $\quad\quad = n_1$

Distance moved by pulley B $\quad = n_2$

Actual amount of chain taken in $= n_1 - n_2$.

Because of the snatch block the load is raised or lowered by half this amount,

$$\text{i.e. } \frac{n_1 - n_2}{2}$$

$$\text{Velocity ratio} = \frac{\text{distance moved by effort}}{\text{distance moved by load}}$$

$$= \frac{n_1}{\dfrac{n_1 - n_2}{2}}$$

$$= \frac{2n_1}{n_1 - n_2}$$

Note—This machine is so designed that when the effort is removed the load will remain stationary—i.e. the load is unable to overcome the friction in the machine.

If this were not so, the machine would **overhaul,** that is, it would run backwards when the effort is removed. Overhauling only takes place if the load can overcome the friction in the machine and this can happen when the machine efficiently is more than 50%.

Overhauling

If the efficiency of a machine is less than 50%, more than half the effort is used to overcome friction so that the force used to lift the load is less than the force of friction. When the effort is removed the load exerts, via the machine, a force equal and opposite to that required to lift it. Since this is less than friction, it is not enough to cause motion.

Examples of machines which do not normally overhaul are the Weston Differential Block and Tackle, the worm and wormwheel, and the screw jack.

The Worm and Worm-wheel

This machine, Fig. 221, consists of two main parts:—

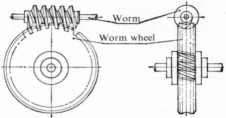

FIG. 221

1. The **worm** is a cylinder with a helical thread cut in its periphery. It is possible to produce more than one thread at a time on the worm. As many as 6 or even 8 may be cut at once.

2. The **worm-wheel.** The periphery of the worm-wheel is made concave—the radius of curvature to suit the worm—and the teeth cut to the helix angle of the worm. The relative position of the axes is right angles and the worm is prevented from axial movement by its bearings.

Single-start worm

In 1 revolution of the worm, the worm-wheel moves round 1 tooth.

Two-start worm

In 1 revolution of the worm, the worm-wheel moves round 2 teeth.

'n'-start worm

In 1 revolution of the worm, the worm-wheel moves round n teeth.

Single-start worm

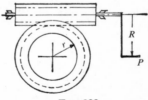

FIG. 222

The accompanying sketch shows a typical worm and worm-wheel arrangement (Fig. 222). The effort P is applied to a cranked handle of radius R attached to the worm spindle. The load or winding drum, radius r, is rigidly attached to the spindle of the worm-wheel of t teeth and the cord attached to the drum.

Let R = radius of crank;

r = radius of drum;

t = number of teeth in worm-wheel.

Consider 1 revolution of the effort P.

Distance moved by the effort = $2\pi R$.

Worm also makes 1 revolution.

Worm-wheel passes 1 tooth = $1/t$ rev.

Winding drum makes $1/t$ revolution.

Rope is wound on $2\pi r \times 1/t$.

i.e. the load is raised a distance $= \dfrac{2\pi r}{t}$

Velocity ratio = $\dfrac{\text{distance moved by effort}}{\text{distance moved by load}} = \dfrac{2\pi R}{2\pi r/t}$

$= \dfrac{Rt}{r}$ or $= \dfrac{Dt}{d}$

For a worm of 'n' starts

One revolution of the worm will cause the worm-wheel to pass n teeth.

Consider 1 revolution of effort.

Distance moved by effort = $2\pi R$.

Worm also makes 1 revolution.

Worm wheel passes n teeth ($1/t \times n$ rev.).

Winding drum makes $1/t \times n$ rev.

Rope is wound on $2\pi rn/t$

i.e. load is raised a distance $= \dfrac{2\pi rn}{t}$

Velocity ratio = $\dfrac{\text{distance moved by effort}}{\text{distance moved by load}} = \dfrac{2\pi R}{2\pi rn/t}$

$= \dfrac{Rt}{rn}$ or $= \dfrac{Dt}{dn}$

Example

Calculate the V.R. for a worm and worm-wheel with the following specifications:—

Worm—three start, worm-wheel—120 teeth,

Radius of drum $= r = 60$ mm

Radius of handle $= R = 250$ mm

$$\text{Velocity ratio} = \frac{\text{distance moved by effort}}{\text{distance moved by load}}$$

$$= \frac{Rt}{rn}$$

$$= \frac{250 \times 120}{60 \times 3}$$

$$= \textbf{166·7}$$

Hoisting winch or crab winch

These machines are used for lifting comparatively heavy masses by an effort such as can be exerted by hand.

They are divided into two groups—the first employs a simple gear train and the unit is termed a single purchase crab winch (Fig. 223).

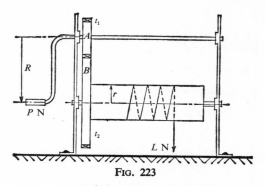

FIG. 223

The effort (*P*) is applied to a cranked handle rigidly fixed to the spindle of the crank gear *A*. The crank gear meshes with a second gear *B* to which is rigidly fixed the winding drum. Rotation of the drum causes the rope to be wound on or off depending on the direction of rotation.

The unit is mounted in a frame having bearings which carry the gear spindles.

Condider one revolution of the effort P.

Distance moved by $P = 2\pi R$

Gear A also makes   1 rev.

Gear B makes $\dfrac{t_1}{t_2}$ rev.

Winding drum makes $\dfrac{t_1}{t_2}$ rev.

Rope is wound on $\dfrac{t_1}{t_2} \times 2\pi r$

$$\text{V.R.} = \frac{\text{distance moved by effort}}{\text{distance moved by load}}$$

$$= \frac{2\pi R}{\dfrac{t_1}{t_2} \times 2\pi r}$$

$$= \frac{t_2 R}{t_1 r} \text{ or } \frac{t_2 D}{t_1 d}$$

The second group employs a compound gear train and is known as a double purchase crab winch (Fig. 224).

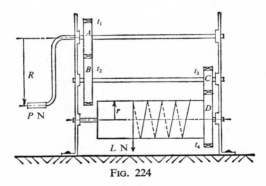

Fig. 224

It has the advantage of being able to have a high V.R. without the use of large and cumbersome gears. Otherwise the construction is similar to that of the single purchase winch.

Gears B and C are fixed to a common spindle.

Consider one revolution of effort P.

Distance moved by $P = 2\pi R$

Gear A also makes 1 rev.

Gear B makes $\quad \dfrac{t_1}{t_2}$ rev.

Gear C makes $\quad \dfrac{t_1}{t_2}$ rev.

Gear D makes $\quad \dfrac{t_1}{t_2} \times \dfrac{t_3}{t_4}$ rev.

Winding drum makes $\dfrac{t_1}{t_2} \times \dfrac{t_3}{t_4}$ rev.

Rope is wound on $\quad \dfrac{t_1}{t_2} \times \dfrac{t_3}{t_4} \times 2\pi r$

$$\text{V.R.} = \frac{\text{distance mobed by effort}}{\text{distance moved by load}} = \frac{2\pi R}{\dfrac{t_1}{t_2} \quad \dfrac{t_3}{t_4} \times 2\pi r}$$

$$= \frac{R \times t_2 \times t_4}{r \times t_1 \times t_3}$$

$$\text{or} = \frac{D \times t_2 \times t_4}{d \times t_1 \times t_3}$$

Note—The diameter of the rope has been neglected. In practical machines this will not be so. The effect of the rope is to increase the effective diameter of the winding drum. This increase in diameter is equal to the diameter of the rope, i.e. effective Radius R = radius of drum + radius of rope (Fig. 225).

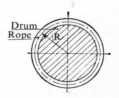

Fig. 225

The bicycle

The bicycle mechanism is a combination of two simple machines, namely the pedal and crank gear and the road wheel and its gear (Fig. 226).

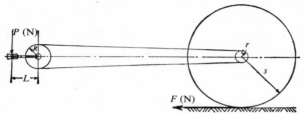

FIG. 226

Let length of crank $= L$ mm

Let radius of crank gear $= R$ mm

Let radius of road wheel $= S$ mm

Let radius of road wheel gear $= r$ mm

Let effort $= P$ N

Let resistance to motion $= F$ N

The effort applied to the pedal produces a moment about the spindle of the pedal gear and is balanced by the force in the chain (Fig. 227).

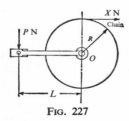

FIG. 227

By taking moments about O,

$$(x \times R) = (P \times L)$$

$$\therefore x = \frac{PL}{R} \text{ or } P = \frac{xR}{L}$$

This force X is transmitted via the chain to the road wheel gear to produce yet another moment and is balanced by the moment produced by the resistance to motion F ("load") at the road (Fig. 228).

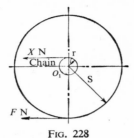

FIG. 228

By taking moments about O_1

$$(F \times S) = (x \times r)$$

$$\therefore F = \frac{xr}{S}$$

Consider one revolution of the pedal,

P (effort) moves $2\pi L$

Pedal gear also makes 1 rev.

Road wheel gear makes $\dfrac{R}{r}$ rev.

Road wheel makes R/r rev.

$\therefore$ Distance moved by road wheel $= \dfrac{R}{r} \times 2\pi S$

$$= \frac{2\pi RS}{r}$$

$$\text{V.R.} = \frac{\text{distance moved by effort}}{\text{distance moved by load}} = \frac{2\pi L}{\dfrac{2\pi RS}{r}}$$

$$= \frac{Lr}{RS}$$

The Law of the Machine

When two quantities are plotted together in a graphical form and the result is a straight line, the relationship between the two can be expressed by the mathematical equation of a straight line,

i.e. $Y = mX + c$ where Y is the value on the OY axis,
X is the value on the OX axis,
m is the gradient of the line,
and c is a constant.

The two quantities we are going to consider are the effort and the load. Since it is usual to plot the effort on the OY axis and the load on the OX axis, our symbols for load and effort—L and P—will replace X and Y respectively.

When, in machine experiments, the load and its corresponding effort are expressed as a graph, the result is a straight line. It can, therefore, be represented by a straight line equation and its equation is generally expressed as $P = aL + b$,

where $P =$ applied effort in newtons,
$L =$ corresponding load in newtons,
$a =$ the gradient of the line,
and $b =$ a constant.

The constant b is the value on the effort axis cut by the load V effort graph and it represents the effort required to operate the machine when there is no load.

This equation is known as the **law of the machine.** If the gradient of the line and the constant are known, then for any given load the corresponding effort may be readily obtained.

In order to establish the values of a and b, one of two methods may be adopted.

Method 1

From experimental data, plot the load V effort graph and select two efforts and their corresponding loads. Substitute these values in the equation $P = aL + b$ and solve as two simultaneous equations for a and b.

Method 2

Select two points P and Q on the graph and read off the values of x and y (Fig. 229). Since a is the gradient of the line, $a = y/x$, and the value of b can be read directly from the graph.

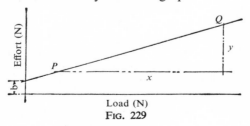

Load (N)
Fig. 229

Limiting efficiency

When the efficiency V load graph is plotted, we notice that it rises rapidly and then tends to flatten off. This suggests that the efficiency of a machine increases with the load but will reach a maximum or limiting value. This value is known as the **limiting efficiency.**

$$\text{Efficiency} = \frac{\text{M.A.}}{\text{V.R.}}$$

$$= \frac{\text{load}}{\text{effort}} \times \frac{1}{\text{V.R.}}$$

but from the law of the machine, $P = aL + b$

$$\therefore \text{Efficiency} = \frac{\text{load } (L)}{aL + b} \times \frac{1}{\text{V.R.}}$$

$$= \frac{L}{V(aL + b)}$$

$$= \frac{L}{aLV + bV}$$

dividing by L,

$$= \frac{1}{aV + bV/L}$$

but as L becomes very large, bV/L becomes very small and so can be neglected. Limiting efficiency $= 1/aV$ where a is the gradient of the slope and V the velocity ratio of the machine being considered.

Note—Data obtained from actual experiments is always subject to slight error. The load and effort results found by experiment may not, therefore, produce a straight line when plotted as a graph. In such cases, the "best straight line" is drawn.

The best straight line is the line which passes through the greatest number of points to give an expression of the average of all the results.

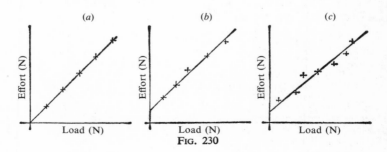

Fig. 230

Fig. 230a shows a graph of the load plotted against the effort for an ideal machine. Since there can be no losses due to friction, etc., in such a machine, all the points lie on one straight line passing through the origin.

Fig. 230b. In the results used to plot this graph, only one or two points lie outside the line and the best straight line has been drawn.

Fig. 230c. Due mainly to a faulty machine—badly fitted bearings, worn gear teeth, etc., nearly all the points lie outside the line. The best straight line has again been drawn but the results as a whole will not give a very true picture of the machine's performance.

Experiments on Machines

In this section, three practical machines are used experimentally to establish the following information:—

(1) The velocity ratio,
(2) The relationship between load and effort,
(3) The efficiency,
(4) The law of the machine,
(5) The limiting efficiency.

All the results should be noted in a table and any working necessary shown neatly and clearly.

Experiment 1

Object: *To find the mechanical advantage, velocity ratio, and the efficiency of a simple 2–1 pulley tackle.*

Apparatus: The apparatus is arranged as shown in the sketch, Fig. 231, and consists of the following:—one 2-pulley block, one single-pulley block, one length of rope to suit the pulleys used; load masses suitable to range from 3 kg to 28 kg, effort masses suitable to range from 2 kg to 15 kg. (For accurate effort reading it is necessary to have a carrier and a series of 0·1 kg masses, ranging from 0 to 1 kg.

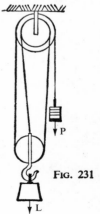

FIG. 231

Procedure: Attach the tackle to a stout beam or rigid bar high enough to allow a fair movement of the effort *P*. Move the effort end of the rope through a known *vertical* distance and, at the same time, measure the corresponding distance moved by the load. The velocity ratio of the system can now be calculated and the result checked. From our previous notes we know the velocity ratio is 3.

Attach a load of mass 3 kg to the hook on the lower block and a trial effort mass to the free end of the rope. Adjust the effort mass so that the load rises slowly and at a uniform rate. When this is achieved, record in the table the value of the load (including the mass of the lower block, in this case 2 kg) and the mass of its corresponding effort.

These results are all recorded in the table and the experiment repeated for all the loads.

We can now calculate the load L, effort P, mechanical advantage, work input, work output, and the efficiency of the machine for each load.

Results

Measured Velocity Ratio

Distance moved by effort $= 1\,000$ mm $= 1 \cdot 0$ m
Distance moved by load $= \quad 333$ mm $= 0 \cdot 333$ m

$$\text{Velocity ratio} = \frac{1\,000}{333}$$
$$= 3$$

Velocity ratio by inspection

Number of ropes supporting load $= 3$
Velocity ratio $= 3$

Load (mass) (kg)	Load L (N)	Effort (mass) (kg)	Effort P (N)	MA $=$ L/P	Work Output (J)	Work Input (J)	Efficiency %
5	49	3·5	34·3	1·43	16·3	34·3	47·5
10	98·1	5·5	53·9	1·82	32·7	53·9	60·6
15	147·1	7·6	74·5	1·97	49·0	74·5	65·7
20	196·2	9·7	95·2	2·07	65·4	95·2	68·9
25	245·2	11·6	114·0	2·16	81·7	114·0	71·6
30	294·3	13·7	134·5	2·19	98·1	134·5	73·0

Specimen calculations

Mechanical advantage $=$ load/effort $= \dfrac{49}{34 \cdot 3}$ $= \mathbf{1 \cdot 43}$

Work input $=$ effort $\times$ distance moved $= 34 \cdot 3 \times 1 = \mathbf{34 \cdot 3\ J}$

Work output $=$ load $\times$ distance moved $= 49 \times 3$ $= \mathbf{16 \cdot 3\ J}$

Efficiency % $= \dfrac{\text{work output}}{\text{work input}} \times 100$ $= \dfrac{16 \cdot 3}{34 \cdot 3} \times 100 = \mathbf{47 \cdot 5\%}$

Note—The calculations are based on the effort moving through a distance of 1 m; the load, therefore, moves through 0·333 m.

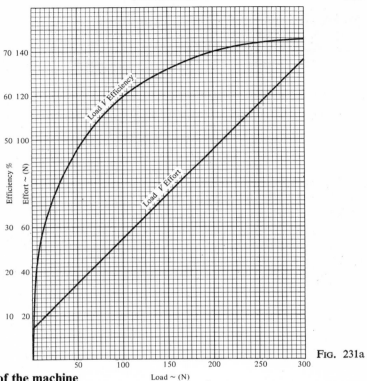

Fɪɢ. 231a

Law of the machine

From graph $\sim$ when $P = 120\ N$ $L = 260$ N

$\qquad\qquad\qquad\quad P =\ 80$ N $L = 162\cdot5$ N

$$P = aL + b$$
$$120 = 260a + b \qquad\qquad (1)$$
$$80 = 162\cdot5a + b \qquad\qquad (2)$$

Subtract $40 = 97\cdot5a$

$$a = \frac{40}{97\cdot5}$$
$$= 0\cdot41$$

Put $a = 0\cdot41$ in equation (1)

$$120 = 106\cdot6 + b$$
$$\therefore b = 13\cdot4$$

$\therefore$ Law of machine is $\mathbf{P = 0\cdot41L + 13\cdot4}$

$N.B.$—P and L are measured in newtons.

Limiting efficiency

$$\text{Limiting efficiency} = \frac{1}{aV}$$
$$= \frac{1}{0\cdot41 \times 3}$$
$$= \frac{1}{1\cdot23}$$
$$= 0\cdot8196$$
$$= \mathbf{81\cdot96\%}$$

Experiment 2

Object: To find the velocity ratio, mechanical advantage, and the efficiency of the simple wheel and axle.

Apparatus: The apparatus consists of a simple wheel and axle, cord, load masses at intervals 0·25 kg from 0·25 kg to 2·5 kg and effort masses—a selection of 0·1 kg and 0·01 kg masses with a suitable carrier. The arrangement of the apparatus is shown in the sketch (Fig. 232).

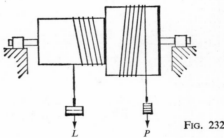

L   P   FIG. 232

Procedure: The cord is wound on to the axle so that, as the effort cord is unwound from the wheel, the load-cord is wound on to the axle.

The velocity ratio can be found by allowing the effort cord to be lowered a given distance and measuring the distance through which the load rises during this time. The result should be checked by using the formula V.R. = R/r.

With the first load mass of 0·25 kg in position, add sufficient mass to the effort carrier so that it is just able to raise the load at a steady rate. This load mass and its corresponding effort mass are recorded in the table. Repeat the experiment for all the loads and tabulate the results. We are now in a position to derive the load *L*, effort *P*, mechanical advantage, work input, work output and the efficiency.

Results

Measured velocity ratio

Distance moved by effort $= 1\ 000$ mm $= 1$ m

Distance moved by load $=\ \ 500$ mm $= 0.5$ m

$$\text{Velocity ratio} = \frac{1\ 000}{500}$$

$$= 2$$

Calculated velocity ratio

Radius of wheel $(R) = 150$ mm

Radius of axle $(r) =\ \ 75$ mm

$$\text{Velocity ratio} = \frac{R}{r}$$

$$= \frac{150}{75}$$

$$= 2$$

Load (mass) (kg)	Load L (N)	Effort (mass) (kg)	Effort P (N)	MA $= L/P$	Work Output (J)	Work Input (J)	Efficiency %
0·25	2·45	0·18	1·76	1·39	1·22	1·76	69·4
0·50	4·91	0·31	3·02	1·63	2·45	3·02	80·5
0·75	7·36	0·43	4·22	1·75	3·68	4·22	87·3
1·00	9·81	0·56	5·50	1·79	4·91	5·50	89·3
1·25	12·28	0·68	6·67	1·84	6·14	6·67	92·0
1·50	14·72	0·81	7·95	1·86	7·36	7·95	92·6
1·75	17·2	0·93	9·13	1·88	8·60	9·13	94·2
2·00	19·62	1·10	10·80	1·85	9·81	10·80	91·0
2·25	22·1	1·18	11·58	1·95	11·05	11·58	95·4
2·50	24·47	1·29	12·70	1·94	12·23	12·7	96·3

Specimen calculations

Mechanical advantage $\ =\ $ load/effort $= 2.45/1.76\ =$ **1·39**

Work input $\ =$ effort $\times$ distance moved $= 1.76 \times 1\ =$ **1·76 J**

Work output $=$ load $\ \times$ distance moved $= 2.45 \times 0.5 =$ **1·22 J**

Efficiency $\% = \dfrac{\text{work output}}{\text{work input}} \times 100 \qquad = \dfrac{1.22}{1.76} \times 100 = $ **69·4%**

Note—The calculations are based on the effort moving through a distance of 1 m; the load, therefore, moves through 0·5 m.

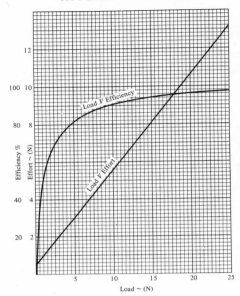

FIG. 232a

Law of Machine

From graph $\sim$ when $P = 13 \cdot 2$ N $L = 25$ N

$\qquad\qquad\qquad\qquad\quad \cdot P = \quad 3 \cdot 0$ N $L = 5 \cdot 0$ N

$$P = aL + b$$

$$13 \cdot 2 = 25a + b \qquad . \qquad . \qquad . \qquad . \qquad (1)$$

$$3 \cdot 0 = \quad 5a + b \qquad . \qquad . \qquad . \qquad . \qquad (2)$$

Subtract $10 \cdot 2 = 20a$

$$a = 0 \cdot 51$$

Put $a = 0 \cdot 51$ in equation (2)

$$\therefore 3 = 2 \cdot 55 + b$$

$$\therefore b = 0 \cdot 45$$

$\therefore$ Law of machine is $\mathbf{P = 0 \cdot 51L + 0 \cdot 45}$

$N.B.$—P and L are measured in newtons.

Limiting efficiency

$$\text{Limiting efficiency} = \frac{1}{aV}$$

$$= \frac{1}{0.51 \times 2}$$

$$= \frac{1}{1.02}$$

$$= 0.98$$

$$= \mathbf{98\%}$$

Experiment 3

Object: To find the velocity ratio, mechanical advantage, and the efficiency of a screw jack.

Apparatus: The apparatus consists of an experimental screw jack, load masses ranging from 2 kg to 20 kg at intervals of 2 kg and effort masses ranging from 0·25 kg to 1·50 kg. These should be a selection of 0·1 kg and 0·01 kg masses, with a suitable carrier.

The experimental screw jack has a flat circular platform rigidly attached to the screw. The load mass is placed centrally on top of the platform and the effort mass is supported by a cord wound round it. A guide pulley ensures that the effort remains clear of the jack body but in no way influences the effect of the effort.

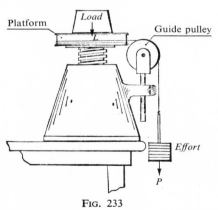

FIG. 233

Method: With no load on the platform, attach sufficient masses to the effort carrier to enable the platform to revolve at a slow uniform rate. This effort—for no load—is recorded in the table of results.

With the 2 kg mass now in position, the effort is readjusted to give again a slow steady rise of the platform. The mass of this effort with the mass of its corresponding load is recorded. By repeating with load increments of 2 kg, a series of results is obtained.

The velocity ratio may be calculated from the actual measurements of the distance moved by the effort and the corresponding distance moved by the load. This can be checked by the formula derived earlier in the study of machines. i.e. V.R. = circumference of platform/pitch of screw.

Results

  Measured Velocity Ratio

$$\text{Distance moved by effort} = 520 \text{ mm}$$

$$\text{Distance moved by load} = 13 \text{ mm (1 pitch)}$$

$$\text{Velocity ratio} = \frac{520}{13}$$

$$= \mathbf{40}$$

Calculated velocity ratio

$$\text{Effective diameter of platform} = 166\cdot5 \text{ mm}$$

$$\text{Pitch of screw} = 13 \text{ mm}$$

$$\text{Velocity ratio} = \frac{\pi D}{p}$$

$$= \frac{\pi \times 166\cdot5}{13}$$

$$= \mathbf{40\cdot2}$$

Load (mass) (kg)	Load L (N)	Effort (mass) (kg)	Effort P (N)	MA = L/P	Work Output (J)	Work Input (J)	Efficiency %
0	0	0·25	2·45	0	0	1·275	0
2	19·62	0·40	3·92	5·0	0·255	2·040	12·5
4	39·24	0·52	5·10	7·7	0·512	2·646	19·2
6	58·86	0·65	6·38	9·23	0·765	3·320	23·1
8	78·48	0·78	7·65	10·25	1·018	4·030	25·3
10	98·10	0·90	8·83	11·10	1·275	4·595	27·7
12	117·72	1·00	9·81	12·00	1·520	5·100	29·8
14	137·34	1·10	10·80	12·73	1·785	5·620	31·8
16	156·96	1·20	11·78	13·35	2·02	6·120	33·3
18	176·58	1·30	12·76	13·85	2·295	6·630	34·6
20	196·20	1·40	13·76	14·30	2·550	7·160	35·7

Specimen calculations

Mechanical advantage = load/effort   = 19·62/3·92
   = **5**

Work input   = effort × distance moved = 3·92 × 0·520
   = **2·04 J**

Work output = load × distance moved = 19·62 × 0·013
   = **0·255 J**

Efficiency % = $\dfrac{\text{Work output}}{\text{Work input}} \times 100$ = $\dfrac{0·255}{2·04} \times 100$
   = **12·5%**

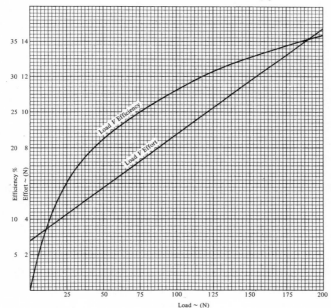

FIG. 233a

Law of machine

From graph ∼ when $P = 11·8$ N $L = 150$ N
             $P = \;5·8$ N $L = \;\;50$ N

$P = aL + b$

$11·8 = 150a + b$.   .   .   .   (1)

$5·8 = \;\;50a + b$.   .   .   .   (2)

Subtract $6 = 100a$

    ∴ $a = 0·06$

G

Put $a = 0.06$ in equation (2)

$$5.8 = 3 + b$$

$$\therefore b = 2.8$$

$\therefore$ Law of m/c is $P = 0.06L + 2.5$

Limiting efficiency

$$\text{Limiting efficiency} = \frac{1}{aV}$$

$$= \frac{1}{0.06 \times 40}$$

$$= \frac{1}{2.4}$$

$$= 0.4167$$

$$= \mathbf{41.67\%}$$

EXERCISES

1. What is meant by the term "mechanical advantage"?

    In a test on a simple machine it is found that an effort of 200 N can just raise a load of mass 200 kg. Calculate the mechanical advantage of the machine.

2. What is meant by "velocity ratio"?

    The measured distance moved by the load of a certain machine is found to be 700 mm. During this movement of the load the effort is displaced 4 m. Find the velocity ratio of the machine.

3. If the calculated velocity ratio of a machine is found to be 20 and the load is restricted to a movement of 20 mm, how far will the effort have to move?

4. What is meant by the efficiency of a machine?

    A double-purchase crab winch produced the following results under test:—

$$\text{Applied effort} = 80 \text{ N}$$
$$\text{Test load} = 140 \text{ kg}$$
$$\text{Displacement of effort} = 1.25 \text{ m}$$
$$\text{Displacement of load} = 50 \text{ mm}$$

From these results calculate:
- (1) The work put into the machine.
- (2) The work got out of the machine.
- (3) The overall efficiency of the machine.

5. Design a simple rope-pulley system which will have a V.R. of 5. If the maximum load to be overcome is 2 000 N and the efficiency of the system is 45%, calculate the maximum effort needed.

6. A simple wheel and axle has an axle radius of 75 mm and an effective wheel radius of 150 mm. If an effort of 50 N is used to raise a certain load and the machine is known to be 0·75 efficient, calculate the mass of this load.

7. Calculate the velocity ratio of a Weston differential block and tackle whose larger pulley has 12 recesses and whose smaller pulley has 11 recesses. If the efficiency of this machine is 34% what load in kg can be lifted by an effort of 440 N?

8. A Weston differential pulley block is designed to have 13 recesses in its larger pulley and 12 recesses in its smaller pulley. What effort would be required to raise a load of mass 400 kg if the efficiency at this load is 30%?

9. Fig. 234 shows a simple gear train. Calculate the velocity ratio of the train and, if gear A rotates in a clockwise direction, state the direction of motion of gear D.

10. A manufacturer provides a machine with interchangeable gears. When supplied the following sizes of gears are included, $20t$, $35t$, $40t$, $50t$. Calculate the twelve possible velocity ratios if the gears are meshed to give a simple train in each case.

11. The velocity ratio of a simple gear train is known to be 6. If the driving gear has 20 teeth, calculate the number of teeth in the driven.

If the driver revolves at 300 rev/min, find the speed of the driven gear.

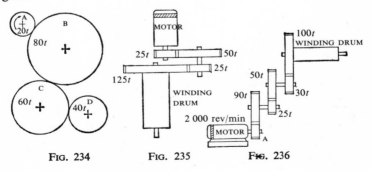

FIG. 234   FIG. 235   FIG. 236

12. An electric motor running at 500 rev/min is used in a small lifting crab. If the compound gear train shown in Fig. 235 is inserted between the motor and the winding drum, find the speed in rev/min of the winding drum.

13. Calculate the number of teeth required in the driving gear *A* of the machine shown in Fig. 236 if the winding drum runs at 100 rev/min.

14. Two gears in mesh transmit 4 kW. The driver runs at 200 rev/min and has 80 teeth of 20 mm pitch. Ignoring friction, calculate the force between the teeth.

15. A gear in mesh with a rack has 60 teeth of 10 mm. How far will the rack move in one revolution of the gear wheel?

Calculate the distance covered per min. by the rack if the gear rotates first in one direction and then in the other, at a rate of 120 rev/min.

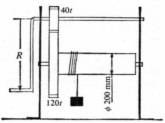

FIG. 237

16. In the machine shown in Fig. 237 what will be the length of handle arm (*R*) necessary to produce a velocity ratio of 12?

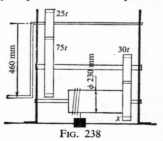

FIG. 238

17. A double-purchase crab winch is shown in Fig. 238. If the required V.R. is 16, calculate the number of teeth in the winding-drum gear.

18. It is found by experiment that the law of the machine for a hand operated screw jack is $P = 0\cdot02L + 0\cdot2$. Calculate the load *L* (kg) which can be raised by an effort *P* of 15 N.

If the V.R. is designed to be 110, calculate
- (1) The mechanical advantage.
- (2) The efficiency.
- (3) The limiting efficiency for these conditions.

19. A window cleaner's cradle is raised and lowered by a single start worm and worm wheel. The worm wheel has 30 teeth and the winding drum has an effective diameter of 160 mm. If the winding handle attached to the worm has a radius of 175 mm, calculate
- (1) The velocity ratio of the device.
- (2) The number of turns of the handle necessary to raise the cradle 2·4 m.

20. A builder's screw jack is designed to raise a load of mass 500 kg. If an effort of 80 N is applied at the end of the effort bar 400 mm long, and the efficiency is 0·25, calculate the greatest pitch necessary for the screw.

21. Fig. 239 illustrates an experimental worm and worm-wheel arrangement. If the efficiency is to be maintained at 80% and the mass of the load at 50 kg, calculate the velocity ratios produced by
- (a) a single-start worm,
- (b) a double-start worm,
- (c) a treble-start worm.

Also calculate the corresponding efforts.

22. Establish the law of the machine when it is known that an effort of 40 N raises a load of mass 17·25 kg, and an effort of 160 N raises a load of mass 85·25 kg.

If the velocity ratio of the machine is 17, calculate the efficiency for a load of mass 90 kg and determine the limiting efficiency of this machine.

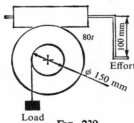

FIG. 239

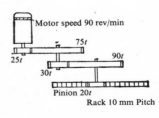

FIG. 240

23. A water-tight door in a ship's bulkhead is operated by a rack and pinion. The drive to the pinion is made through a compound gear train coupled to an electric motor (Fig. 240).

Calculate the time taken to close the door if it is 1 250 mm wide.

24. The velocity ratio of a hand operated winch is 47. The efforts required to raise various loads are given in the table.

Load (kg)	20	30	50	70	90	100
Effort (N)	14	18	26	34	42	46

(a) Draw the graph of the load V effort.
(b) Establish the law of the machine.
(c) Find the value of the Limiting Efficiency of this machine.

CHAPTER VIII

MATERIALS

STRENGTH OF MATERIALS

Elastic and plastic behaviour

When a force acts on a piece of soft clay or putty, the material is deformed under the action of the force, and when the force is removed the material remains deformed. We say that this is plastic behaviour and that the material has undergone plastic deformation.

If a force acts on a piece of spring steel, however, it causes a deformation, but when the force is removed the steel returns to its original shape provided that it has not been deformed too far. This is known as elastic behaviour. **When an elastic body is deformed, forces arise inside the material which resist the external force.** In this condition the material is said to be in a state of stress and the internal forces acting over the cross-sectional area of the material is a measure of the stress in the body. It is these internal forces that return the body to its original shape when the external forces are removed.

Measurement of stress

Consider the bar AB, made of mild steel and fixed rigidly at A with a force of 2 000 N pulling at end B (Fig. 241).

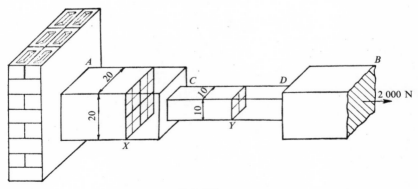

Fig. 241

191

If we increase the load sufficiently, the bar will break and obviously the break will occur across a section between C and D, say on section Y. Now the same load will act on section X as on section Y, but since the area of section Y is smaller, the intensity of load on the metal at this section will be greater. Each of the sections may be divided into small units of area and, if we take the intensity of load on a unit of area of the section, we shall have a measure of the stress in the material at that section.

In part CD the whole force of 2 000 N is resisted by the metal of cross-sectional area 100 mm². We can say then that the stress in the bar at this part is 20 N to one mm² or 20 N/mm² = 20×10^6 N/m².

In part AC the 2 000 N is resisted by 400 mm² so that each square millimetre carries a load of only $2\,000 \div 400 = 5$ N/mm² = 5×10^6 N/m².

i.e. Stress on any cross section in part $AC = 5 \times 10^6$ N/m².

If the load is measured in newtons and the cross-sectional area in mm², the stress is measured in N/mm². If the load is in newtons and the area in m², the stress is measured in N/m².

Thus, knowing the total load and the cross-sectional area over which it is acting, we can calculate the stress in that section by dividing the load by the area.

i.e. $$\text{Stress (N/m}^2) = \frac{\text{load (N)}}{\text{area (m}^2)}$$

Example 1

Calculate the compressive stress in a square cast iron column of side 0·05 m when it resists a force of 2 400 N (Fig. 242).

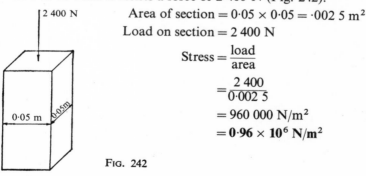

Area of section = $0·05 \times 0·05 = ·002\ 5$ m²

Load on section = 2 400 N

$$\text{Stress} = \frac{\text{load}}{\text{area}}$$

$$= \frac{2\ 400}{0·002\ 5}$$

$$= 960\ 000 \text{ N/m}^2$$

$$= \mathbf{0·96 \times 10^6 \text{ N/m}^2}$$

2 400 N

0·05 m   0·05 m

FIG. 242

Example 2

A 50 mm diameter bar of mild steel is subjected to a load of 6 kN. Find the stress in the bar (Fig. 243).

Area of bar section $= \frac{\pi}{4}D^2$

$$= \frac{\pi}{4} \times 50^2$$

$$= 1\ 964 \text{ mm}^2$$

$$= \mathbf{1 \cdot 96 \times 10^{-3} \ m^2}$$

Stress in the bar $= \dfrac{\text{load}}{\text{area}}$

$$= \frac{6 \times 10^3}{1 \cdot 96 \times 10^{-3}}$$

$$= \frac{6}{1 \cdot 96} \times 10^6 = \mathbf{3 \cdot 06 \times 10^6 \ N/m^2}$$

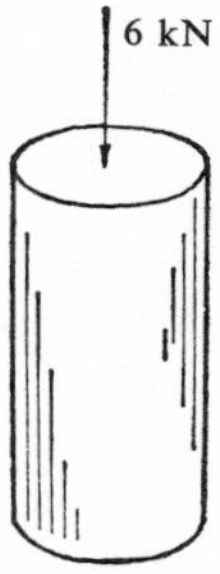

6 kN

FIG. 243

Example 3

A mild steel tube of outside diameter 30 mm and inside diameter 20 mm carries a load of mass 900 kg. Find the stress in the material (Fig. 244).

Mass carried $= 900$ kg
Force resisted $= 900 \times 9 \cdot 81$
$\quad\quad\quad\quad\quad = 8\ 829$ N

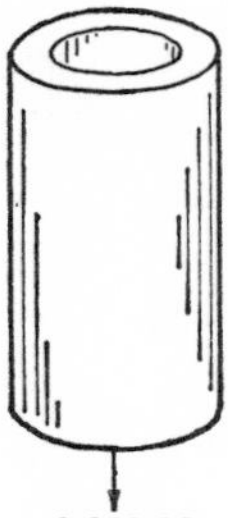

8 829 N
FIG. 244

Area of tube section $= \frac{\pi}{4}D^2 - \frac{\pi}{4}d^2$

$$= \frac{\pi}{4}30^2 - \frac{\pi}{4}20^2$$

$$= \frac{\pi}{4}(30^2 - 20^2)$$

$$= \frac{500\pi}{4} = 392 \text{ mm} = \mathbf{3 \cdot 92 \times 10^{-4} \ m^2}$$

Stress in the material $= \dfrac{\text{load}}{\text{area}} = \dfrac{8 \cdot 829 \times 10^3}{3 \cdot 92 \times 10^{-4}}$

$$= \mathbf{22 \cdot 52 \times 10^6 \ N/m^2}$$

Strain

When a force acts on an elastic body, it causes the body to be deformed. The deformation may take the form of stretching, compressing, twisting, etc., and when the body is deformed in this way it is said to be in strain.

If a mild steel bar, 120 mm long, is subjected to an external force which stretches it by 0·2 mm the bar is in strain (Fig. 245).

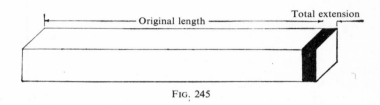

Fig. 245

The bar consists of a 120 mm length of metal so that each mm of the bar stretches

$$\frac{0 \cdot 2}{120} \text{ mm} = 0 \cdot 001 \ 67 \text{ mm}$$

i.e. when the force acts on this bar, each mm of the bar stretches 0·001 67 mm and the whole bar stretches 0·001 67 of its length. For example a length of $\frac{1}{0 \cdot 001 \ 67}$ of this bar would stretch 1 mm under the action of this force.

This fraction 0·001 67 is the measure of the strain in the bar caused by *this* force.

i.e.   The strain in the bar $= 0 \cdot 001 \ 67 = \dfrac{\text{extension of the bar}}{\text{original length of the bar}}$

Since the force tends to stretch the bar, the bar is in tension

$$\text{and tensile strain} = \frac{\text{extension}}{\text{original length of the bar}}$$

When the force is made to act in the opposite direction, the bar is then in compression and decreases in length under the action of the force so that

$$\text{compressive strain} = \frac{\text{compression}}{\text{original length}}$$

$$\text{In general terms} \quad \textbf{strain} = \frac{\textbf{change in length}}{\textbf{original length}}$$

Since both the change in length and the original length of the bar are units of length, the strain is a number and in practice is always a small fraction. For this reason it is sometimes known as fractional strain.

Hooke's Law

When we started to study forces (in Chap. 1) we saw that we could stretch or compress a steel spring by subjecting it to a force. We saw further that the deformation of the spring was proportional to the force applied to it.

Now the steel from which the spring is made is an elastic material and all such materials behave in a similar fashion when subjected to external forces, i.e. they return to their normal position when the force is removed (provided the force is not too great) and the amount of deformation is proportional to the applied force (again provided that the force is not too great).

The scientist Hooke was the first person to investigate the behaviour of elastic bodies when they were subjected to external forces. He found that if one unit of force caused a certain extension in a body made of an elastic material, two units of force caused exactly double the extension, a force of three units caused three times the extension and so on.

He announced his findings, known as Hooke's law, as follows:—

When an elastic body is subjected to an external force, the deformation produced is proportional to the applied force.

The stiffness of a spring

By Hooke's law the deformation of a spring is proportional to the applied force, so that, for each unit of length the spring is deformed, a certain specific force is required. The force required to extend or compress a spring by one unit of length is a measure of the stiffness of the spring.

For example, if a force of 20 N is required to stretch a spring by 1 mm then the stiffness of the spring is $\frac{20}{0 \cdot 001} = 20\ 000$ N/metre.

The stiffness of a spring may be measured in other units; for example in large heavy springs it may be measured in kN/m, or in small springs in N/mm.

Elasticity

Let us examine a heavy square section bar, of side 50 mm, 300 mm long, subjected to a pull of 50 kN. Under this load the bar stretches 0·45 mm (Fig. 246).

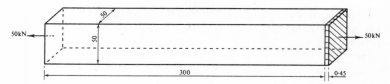

So far, what we know concerns only this particular bar, and in this form we cannot apply the information to any other bar.

But if we consider the material from which the bar is made, and apply what we know to a unit of the material, then we may use our results on any other bar or beam as long as it is made of the same material.

$$\text{Force acting on the bar} = 50 \times 10^3 \text{ N}$$

$$\text{Cross-sectional area of the bar} = 2\ 500 \text{ mm}^2$$

$$= 2\ 500 \times 10^{-6} \text{ m}^2$$

$$\text{Stress in the bar} = \frac{\text{load}}{\text{area}}$$

$$= \frac{50 \times 10^3}{2\ 500 \times 10^{-6}}$$

$$= 20 \times 10^6 \text{ N/m}^2$$

Also   Total length of the bar = 300 mm

Change in length of the bar = 0·45 mm

$$\text{Strain} = \frac{\text{extension}}{\text{original length}}$$

$$= \frac{0·45}{300}$$

$$= \mathbf{0·001\ 5}$$

i.e. the bar increase by 0·001 5 of its length under this force.

Thus if we took a cube of the material of side 1 m and subjected it to a load of 20 MN (i.e. to a stress of 20×10^6 N/m²) the length would increase by 0·001 5 m (i.e. the strain would be 0·001 5, or it would increase by 0·001 5 of its length) (Fig. 247).

When we consider the load and the extension, we are considering factors which affect this bar only but, if we consider the stress the load

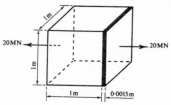

produces and the strain it causes, we are considering the material from which the bar is made—e.g. mild steel—and we can apply our results to any specimen of mild steel of the same composition.

Since there will be no deformation except under load it follows that there can be no strain without a corresponding stress.

Hooke's law states that the deformation of an elastic body is proportional to the force producing it. If we apply this to our one-cubic metre of material, the extension, and therefore, the strain, is proportional to the stress.

$$\text{so that } \frac{\text{stress}}{\text{strain}} = \text{a constant}$$

This constant measures the elasticity of the material, since it compares the force acting on the material to the deformation produced by it.

This ratio was first used by the scientist Young, and the constant is known as Young's modulus of elasticity for the material. It is generally denoted by the letter E.

$$\frac{\text{stress}}{\text{strain}} = E.$$

Since stress is measured in N/m^2 and strain is a number, elasticity is also measured in N/m^2. If the load is measured in MN, the elasticity will be in MN/m^2.

Accurate Measurement

You will appreciate that the stretch of a piece of metal is very small—far too small to be measured with a rule; so, before carrying out any further experiments or observations, we will examine two instruments which engineers use when accurate sizes are required.

1. The micrometer screw gauge

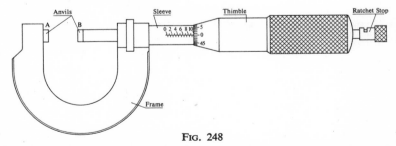

FIG. 248

Fig. 248 shows a modern micrometer screw gauge. It consists of a rigid steel frame carrying a sleeve on which is marked a scale graduated in millimetres. Each millimetre is further divided into two by the scale on the other side of the datum line so that the distance between each two successive marks on the sleeve scale is 0·5 mm.

As the thimble is rotated, anvil *B* is screwed in to meet anvil *A*. The screw carrying the thimble is made in such a way that one turn of the thimble takes it from one mark on the sleeve to the next—i.e. it covers 0·5 mm.

The thimble itself has a scale dividing it into 50 equal parts so that we can measure accurately 1/50 of a turn of the thimble.

One turn of the thimble therefore widens or closes the gap between the anvils by 0·5 mm. But, since one turn of the thimble is divided by the thimble scale into 50 parts, the movement of the anvil can be measured accurately to

$$\frac{1}{50} \times 0\cdot5 = 0\cdot01 \text{ mm.}$$

i.e. for each mark on the thimble scale that passes the datum line, anvil *B* moves 0·01 mm.

Using the micrometer

Put the specimen to be measured between the anvils and screw the thimble until it just grips the specimen lightly. Do not screw it up tight.

To take the reading take the number of marks on the sleeve scale above the datum line—this gives the number of millimetres. The scale below the datum line will determine distances of 0·5 mm since each mark bisects those on the upper scale. If a mark is showing on the lower scale it then shows a further 0·5 mm. To this must be added the reading on the thimble scale (e.g. a reading of 16 on the thimble scale = 0·16 mm).

The sum of these figures gives the micrometer reading to two decimal places so that using the micrometer the size of a specimen can be measured correct to 0·01 mm.

A specimen reading is shown (Fig. 249).

Reading

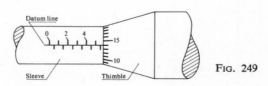

Fig. 249

Number of millimetres shown above the datum line = 5   mm
A further mark is shown below the datum line =   ·5   mm
Divisions on thimble to datum line = 14 =   ·14 mm
∴ **Gap between anvils = 5·64 mm**

Some micrometers are fitted with ratchet devices for ensuring the correct pressure on the specimen, and locking devices for locking the instrument at any desired reading, but in structure and operation they are all basically the same.

With a little practice you will find the micrometer very easy to use. *Read the following micrometer settings* (micrometer to read 0·01 mm).

FIG. 250

2. The vernier gauge

The vernier gauge is shown in Fig. 251. It consists of two strips of metal each marked with a scale. Scale A, the stationary scale, is 20 mm in length and scale B, the moving scale, is 19 mm in length but unlike scale A which is marked off in millimetres scale B is marked off into 20 equal divisions. Thus each division on scale B is $\frac{1}{20}$ mm, i.e. 0·05 mm shorter than each division on scale A.

Now if scale B moves slightly until the first marks on both scales coincide then scale B will have moved 0·05 mm. If it moves until the second marks coincide then scale B will have moved $2 \times 0·05 = 0·1$ mm. This mark on scale B is marked 1 since it denotes that scale B has moved 0·1 mm. Similarly if B is moved until any other numbered mark on scale B coincides with a mark on scale A then the number will denote how far scale B has moved—the number denoting the distance in mm.

Reading the vernier

Set the zero marks opposite each other. If the sliding scale is moved until the 5 mark coincides with a mark on scale A then scale B has moved 0·5 mm. Move scale B slightly further and on examining the mark on scale B which coincides with a mark on scale A, the movement can be measured. By using the unnumbered marks on scale B the movement can be read to 0·05 mm.

Experiment 2

Object: To examine a steel wire under tension and find

(*a*) the stress in the wire;

(*b*) the strain in the wire;

(*c*) the modulus of elasticity for the material from which the wire is made.

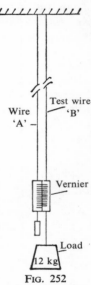

Apparatus: We require two steel wires fixed firmly to an overhead beam, each wire carrying a hook, a vernier gauge, a micrometer screw gauge, and a supply of masses.

Procedure: Hang a small mass on each of the hooks to keep the wires taut and, using the screws provided, fix the stationary vernier scale to wire *A* and the sliding vernier scale to wire *B*, the wire under test. Arrange the scales so that the zero marks coincide.

Measure the diameter of the wire under test using the micrometer screw gauge.

Measure the length of the wire under test from the beam to the vernier gauge.

Add a series of 2 kg masses to the hook on the wire under test and take the vernier reading as each mass is added until the wire carries a load

Fig. 252

of 12 kg. Remove the masses one at a time and take the vernier reading after the removal of each mass. Tabulate your results.

Results

Load (kg)	2	4	6	8	10	12
Force in wire (N)	19·62	39·24	58·86	78·48	98·1	117·72
Extension (loading) (mm)	0·508	1·015	1·52	2·03	2·54	3·04
Extension (unloading) (mm)	0·508	1·015	1·52	2·03	2·54	3·04

$$\text{Dia of wire} = 0{\cdot}698 \text{ mm}$$

$$\text{Cross-sectional area of wire} = \frac{\pi D^2}{4} = \frac{\pi \times 0{\cdot}698^2}{4} = 0{\cdot}382\,4 \text{ mm}^2$$

$$= 0{\cdot}382\,4 \times 10^{-6} \text{ m}^2$$

$$\text{Original length of wire} = 2 \text{ m}$$

Using a sheet of graph paper, choose suitable scales and plot the value of each extension against the load (N) producing it. This will give a series of six points, which should ideally be in a straight line, but which, due to slight experimental inaccuracies, may not be so. Draw the best straight line through the points—this will help to average out the experimental inaccuracies.

Outline of calculation

To calculate the stress, strain, and elasticity we select any convenient point on the graph and use the values of load and extension at that point.

$$\text{Stress} = \frac{\text{load}}{\text{area}} \qquad \text{Strain} = \frac{\text{extension}}{\text{original length}}$$

$$\frac{58{\cdot}86 \times 10^6}{0{\cdot}382\,4} \qquad = \frac{1{\cdot}52}{2\,000}$$

$$= \mathbf{154 \times 10^6 \text{ N/m}^2} \qquad = \mathbf{0{\cdot}000\,76}$$

$$\text{Elasticity of the wire} = \frac{\text{stress}}{\text{strain}}$$

$$= \frac{154 \times 10^6}{0{\cdot}000\,76}$$

$$= \frac{154 \times 10^6}{76 \times 10^{-5}}$$

$$= \mathbf{202.5 \times 10^9 \text{ N/m}^2}$$

Tensile test—mild steel

Object: To study the effect of continued loading on a mild steel specimen and to show, graphically, the general characteristics of mild steel under tension when tested to destruction.

Apparatus: The loads are applied by a specially designed machine, capable of firmly holding the specimen while it is in tension.

Fig. 253 shows the layout of such a machine. The test piece is held in position by self tightening jaws which increase their grip with every increase in load. The lower jaws are attached to the base of the machine

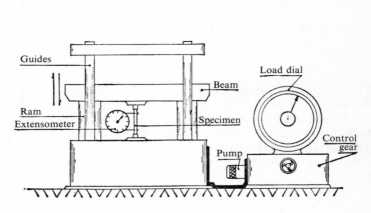

FIG. 253

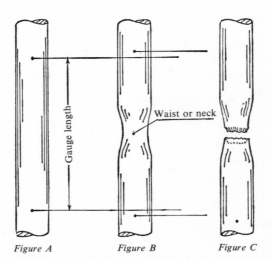

Figure A   *Figure B*   *Figure C*

Figure A:—Specimen between zero load
and proportional limit load

Figure B:—Specimen between yield point load
and breaking load

Figure C:—Specimen after fracture

FIG. 254

and the upper jaws are attached to a beam which can be hydraulically raised or lowered. During the test the force raising the beam—extending the specimen—is recorded on a dial scale graduated in kilo-newtons. On a machine of this type very accurate control can be kept of the applied load.

The cross-sectional shape of the specimen is generally circular and turned to a diameter which will give a simple cross-sectional area.

e.g. $11\cdot3$ mm diameter gives an area of 100 mm^2 = $0\cdot0001$ m^2

The overall length of the specimen is determined by the capacity of the testing machine and does not enter into the test calculations. The actual test length of the specimen is a gauged or measured distance, marked on the surface of the specimen by two light centre-punch marks. This is the **gauge length** or the **original length** and is generally taken as 50 or 100 mm spaced centrally along the overall length of the specimen.

The extension produced by each load increment is measured by an extensometer. This is an instrument capable of recording very small changes in dimension—in this case length. One common type of extensometer is in the form of a dial gauge attached to two clamps. One of these clamps is given a restricted movement away from the other and, as it moves, it causes a pointer on the dial to be deflected. The dial may be graduated to read in mm or as scale readings which must be converted into mm before being used in the calculations.

Method: The prepared specimen is securely clamped in the jaws of the testing machine and the beam raised to take up the "slack". The extensometer is now fitted so that the fixing set screw in each clamp fits into the centre-punch marks on the specimen. The extensions recorded will be over the gauge length—in this case 50 mm. The range of the extensometer used is from zero to $0\cdot5$ mm. When the extension of the gauge length reaches $0\cdot5$ mm the extensometer is removed and extensions beyond this amount are measured by placing the points of dividers into the gauge marks, and measuring the distance between the divider points with an engineer's rule.

Loads are now applied in as near equal increments as possible, and the extension produced by each load is noted.

It is most important that once the loading has commenced it should continue without interruption until the specimen breaks.

Results and specimen calculations

Data:—

Diameter of specimen	11·3 mm
Area of specimen .	1×10^{-4} m^2
Gauge length . .	50 mm
Diameter at fracture .	7·8 mm
Area at fracture .	$0·48 \times 10^{-4}$ m^2
Length after fracture .	57·5 mm
Total extension .	3·5 mm
Load at proportional limit . . .	70 kN
Extension at proportional limit . .	0·175 mm
Maximum load .	82 kN
Breaking load . .	54 kN

Ext. (mm)	Load ($\times 10^3$ N)
0·040	16·5
0·062	25·5
0·0805	33·2
0·0927	38·2
0·107	44·0
0·134	55·0
0·188	77·7
0·240	80·0
0·250	80·7
0·252	81·5
0·300	81·3
0·300	81·2
0·400	80·0
0·500	80·8
0·750	82·0
2·080	75·5
2·38	72·0
2·75	67·6
3·17	61·0
3·50	54·0

Calculations

Let load $= P$; original area $= A_1$; final area $= A_2$; gauge length $= L$; extension $= e$; Young's Modulus $= E$;

$$\text{Stress at proportional limit} = \frac{P}{A_1} \times \frac{70 \times 10^3}{1 \times 10^{-4}}$$

$$= 70 \times 10^7 \text{ N/m}^2$$

$$\text{Strain} = \frac{\text{extension}}{\text{original length}} = \frac{0\cdot175}{50}$$

$$= 0\cdot003\ 5$$

$$\text{Elasticity} = \frac{\text{Stress}}{\text{Strain}}$$

$$= \frac{70 \times 10^7}{0\cdot003\ 5}$$

$$= 200 \times 10^9 \text{ N/m}^2$$

$$\text{Maximum load} = 82 \times 10^3 \text{ N}$$

$$\text{Ultimate stress} = \frac{\text{maximum load}}{\text{original area}}$$

$$= \frac{82 \times 10^3}{1 \times 10^4} = 820 \times 10^6 \text{ N/m}^2$$

$$\text{Percentage elongation} = \frac{\text{total extension}}{\text{original length}} \times 100$$

$$= \frac{3\cdot5}{50} \times 100 = 7\%$$

$$\text{Percentage reduction in area} = \frac{\text{change in area}}{\text{original area}} \times 100$$

$$= \frac{(1 - 0\cdot48) \times 10^{-4}}{1 \times 10^{-4}} \times 100$$

$$= 52\%$$

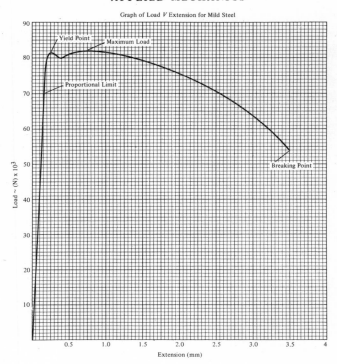

Graph of Load *V* Extension for Mild Steel

Conclusions

From the graph of the load/extension we can see that up to the proportional limit the load is proportional to the extension as stated by Hooke's Law. It follows that, if the applied load is removed, the specimen will return to its original length.

Just beyond the proportional limit the specimen begins to show a marked increase in length for a slight increase in load. The point at which this occurs is known as the **yield point.**

Beyond the yield point the steel "work hardens" and it is found to be capable of withstanding further increases in load. The highest point on the graph is the maximum load to which the specimen can be subjected. It is noticed that from here on the load is decreased and that the extension, even with the decrease in load, is great. This continues till the specimen breaks.

Once the yield point has been reached, it is noticed that the appearance of the specimen begins to alter. It no longer remains cylindrical but shows the formation of a neck or waist. The cross-sectional area of this neck continues to get less as the specimen reaches its breaking point.

The shape of the fractured ends (Fig. 254) is also interesting. One end is cup-shaped and the other cone-shaped and they can be fitted together to produce a perfect joint.

Factor of safety

In the tensile test we saw that the maximum load the specimen could carry acted at the ultimate point, and that the stress at that point is known as the maximum or ultimate stress.

Under normal working conditions the material is never loaded to the ultimate point and in practice the load is always kept so that the material is well within its elastic limit. A maximum working load is fixed so that this is always the case.

The ratio of the maximum load to the safe working load is known as the factor of safety.

$$\text{i.e. Factor of safety} = \frac{\text{maximum load (N)}}{\text{safe working load (N)}}$$

or, since we assume that the cross-sectional area of the metal does not change during this loading,

$$\text{Factor of safety} = \frac{\text{maximum or ultimate stress (N/m}^2\text{)}}{\text{safe working stress (N/m}^2\text{)}}$$

Example 1

A mild steel column of cross-sectional area $2\,600$ mm^2 is required to carry a maximum working load of 200 kN. If the ultimate tensile stress of mild steel is 450 MN/m^2 find the factor of safety of the column.

$$\text{Load} = 200 \text{ kN} = 200 \times 10^3 \text{ N}$$

$$\text{Cross-sectional area} = 2\,600 \text{ mm}^2 = 2\,600 \times 10^{-6} \text{ m}^2$$

$$\text{U.T.S.} = 450 \text{ MN/m}^2 = 450 \times 10^6 \text{ N/m}^2$$

$$\text{Maximum working stress} = \frac{\text{load}}{\text{area}}$$

$$= \frac{200 \times 10^3}{2\,600 \times 10^{-6}}$$

$$= 77 \times 10^6 \text{ N/m}^2$$

$$\text{Factor of safety} = \frac{\text{ultimate tensile stress}}{\text{safe working stress}}$$

$$= \frac{450 \times 10^6}{77 \times 10^6}$$

$$= \mathbf{5 \cdot 85}$$

Example 2

A mild steel bar is required to withstand a pull of 80 kN. Find the diameter of the bar if the U.T.S. of mild steel is 430×10^6 N/m^2 and the factor of safety for the bar is 12.

Load $= 80 \times 10^3$ N

U.T.S. $= 430 \times 10^6$ N/m^2

F.O.S. $= 12$

$$\text{Factor of safety} = \frac{\text{ultimate tensile stress}}{\text{safe working stress}}$$

$$12 = \frac{430 \times 10^6}{\text{safe working stress}}$$

$$\therefore \text{ Safe working stress} = \frac{430 \times 10^6}{12}$$

$$= 35 \cdot 8 \times 10^6 \text{ N/m}^2$$

$$\text{Working stress} = \frac{\text{working load}}{\text{area of section}}$$

$$\therefore \text{ Area of section} = \frac{\text{load}}{\text{stress}}$$

$$= \frac{80 \times 10^3}{35 \cdot 8 \times 10^6}$$

$$= 2 \cdot 24 \times 10^{-3} \text{ m}^2 = 2\,240 \text{ mm}^2$$

$$\frac{\pi D^2}{4} = 2\,240$$

$$\therefore D^2 = 2\,240 \times \frac{4}{\pi}$$

$$= 2\,850$$

$$\therefore D = 53 \cdot 4 \text{ mm}$$

$$\therefore \textbf{Required diameter} = \textbf{53.4 mm}$$

Shear

We have seen how a bar or a piece of machinery may be designed to stand up to a tensile load. This is very useful, but in designing a machine we must make all parts equally strong. For example, Fig 255

FIG. 255

shows a tow bar used for towing heavy vehicles. This bar must be strong enough to take the tensile load required to tow a heavy vehicle, but it would be no use having a very strong bar if the pins in the couplings were weak.

If you examine Fig. 256 you will notice that a load which produces a tensile effect in the bar produces a different effect in the pin.

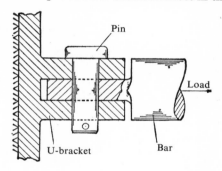

FIG. 256

If the pin is going to break it will do so because a part of the pin will be pulled out between the U-bracket.

When a piece of metal is subjected to a load of this nature it is said to be in shear, i.e. **it is in shear when one section of the metal tends to slide over a neighbouring section.**

Shear stress

In dealing with shear stress we adopt the same rules as with tensile stress. The stress is calculated by comparing the total load to the area carrying it.

$$\text{Shear stress} = \frac{\text{load (N)}}{\text{area subjected to shear (m}^2)}$$

A specimen of the material may be tested in a test machine and the behaviour of the specimen under different loads noted. A graph may be drawn of the results and from this we may find the maximum load the specimen can carry under shear. From this we can find the ultimate shear stress in the material.

$$\text{Ultimate shear stress} = \frac{\text{maximum load (N)}}{\text{area under shear (m}^2)}$$

Also, similar to tensile loading

$$\text{Factor of safety} = \frac{\text{ultimate shear stress (N/m}^2)}{\text{safe working stress (N/m}^2)}$$

Single shear

We say that a pin or rivet is in single shear when the stress is acting on one section only. The rivet shown in Fig. 257 is in single shear.

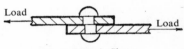

Effect of Single Shear

FIG. 257

Double shear

A bolt or rivet is said to be in double shear when two sections are in shear. Fig. 258 shows a rivet in double shear.

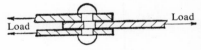

Effect of Double Shear

FIG. 258

Example 1

A 20 mm diameter rivet in single shear is subjected to a load of 50 kN. Find the shear stress in the rivet.

$$\text{shear stress} = \frac{\text{load}}{\text{area subjected to shear}}$$

Load = 50 kN
$\quad$ = 50×10^3 N
Dia. = 20 mm
Area = $\frac{\pi}{4} \times 400$
$\quad$ = 314 mm^2
$\quad$ = 314×10^{-6} m^2

$= \dfrac{50 \times 10^3}{314 \times 10^{-6}}$

$= \dfrac{50 \times 10^3}{31 \cdot 4 \times 10^{-5}}$

$= 1 \cdot 59 \times 10^8$

$= 159 \times 10^6 \text{ N/m}^2$

Example 2

A draw-bar pin of diameter 40 mm is subjected to a pull of 90 kN. If the pin is in double shear, find the stress in the metal.

$$\text{Area under shear} = 2 \times \frac{\pi}{4}D^2$$

Dia. = 40 mm
Load = 90 kN

$$= \frac{\pi}{2} \times 1\ 600 \times 10^{-6}$$

$$= 2\ 512 \times 10^{-6}\ \text{m}^2$$

$$\text{Shear stress} = \frac{\text{load}}{\text{area subjected to shear}}$$

$$= \frac{90 \times 10^3}{2\ 512 \times 10^6}$$

$$= 35 \cdot 8 \times 10^6\ \text{N/m}^2$$

The punching machine

The punching machine is designed to punch holes in metal plates. The die is designed so that the punch just fits neatly into it. Both the punch and the die are made of hardened steel.

The plate is laid on the die and when the punch descends it exerts a shear force on the plate as it punches the hole (Fig. 259).

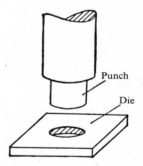

Punch

Die

FIG. 259

As the punch descends on to the plate the metal under shear is the section of the plate round the perimeter of the punch.

i.e. Area of metal under shear = perimeter of the punch × thickness of the metal (Fig. 260).

Area under Shear

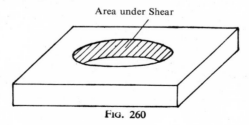

FIG. 260

If we are given the size of the hole, the ultimate shear stress of the metal and the thickness of the plate, we can calculate the force required to drive the punch.

Example 1

Find the force required to punch a 20 mm diameter hole in a 10 mm mild steel plate if the ultimate shear stress of mild steel is 350×10^6 N/m².

Area of metal under shear

$$= \text{circumference of hole} \times \text{thickness of plate}$$
$$= \pi \times 20 \times 10 = 628 \text{ mm} = 628 \times 10^{-6} \text{ m}^2$$
$$\text{Ultimate shear stress} = \frac{\text{load}}{\text{area under shear}}$$
$$350 \times 10^6 = \frac{\text{shear force} \times 10^6}{628}$$
$$\text{Force required} = 350 \times 628$$
$$= 219\ 800 \text{ N}$$
$$= \textbf{219·8 kN}$$

Riveted joints

When a joint is fastened by more than one rivet, the area of all the rivet sections under shear must be added to obtain the *total* area under shear, before calculating the shear stress.

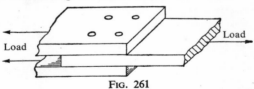

FIG. 261

For example, in the joint shown in Fig. 261, there are four rivets in double shear. That means that the area under shear $= 8 \times \pi D^2/4$ where D is the diameter of the rivet.

When the metal is broken as shown at x in Fig. 262 you will notice that the total load is carried by the four rivets at A and also that the total load is carried by the six rivets at B.

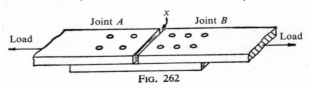

FIG. 262

Example

In the riveted joint shown in Fig. 262, part *A* is held by four 20 mm dia. rivets and part *B* by six 15 mm rivets. If the maximum load allowed on the joint is 80 kN find the factor of safety of the joint. The ultimate shear stress of the material is 380 MN/m² (neglect tensile stresses).

Joint A

$$\text{Area of metal under shear} = 4 \times \frac{\pi}{4} \times 20^2 \times 10^{-6}$$
$$= 400\pi \times 10^{-6}$$
$$= \mathbf{1\ 256 \times 10^{-6}\ m^2}$$

$$\text{Shear stress in the rivets} = \frac{\text{load}}{\text{area}}$$
$$= \frac{80 \times 1\ 000}{1\ 256} \times 10^6$$
$$= \mathbf{63 \cdot 7 \times 10^{-6}\ N/m^2}$$

Joint B

$$\text{Area of metal under shear} = 6 \times \frac{\pi}{4} \times 15^2 \times 10^{-6}$$
$$= 337 \cdot 5\pi \times 10^{-6}$$
$$= 1\ 059 \times 10^{-6}\ m^2$$

$$\text{Shear stress in the rivets} = \frac{\text{load}}{\text{area}}$$
$$= \frac{80 \times 10^3 \times 10^6}{1\ 059}$$
$$= \mathbf{75 \cdot 5 \times 10^6\ N/m^2}$$

Since the highest shear stress occurs in the rivets of joint *B* we must use that value in determining the factor of safety.

$$\text{Factor of safety} = \frac{\text{ultimate shear stress}}{\text{maximum working stress}}$$
$$= \frac{380 \times 10^6}{75 \cdot 5 \times 10^6}$$
$$= 5 \cdot 04$$

Factor of safety of the whole joint = **5·04**

Tensile stress in riveted joints

When a riveted joint is subjected to a pull P as shown in Fig. 263 the rivets are in shear, but the plates are in tension.

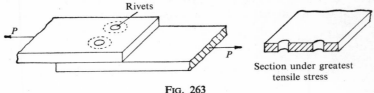

Fig. 263

The greatest tensile stress in the plates occurs across the section of minimum area, i.e. across the rivet holes. This is the area that must be used in calculating the tensile strength of the joint.

Example

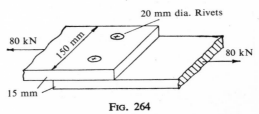

Fig. 264

Fig. 264 shows a riveted joint subjected to a pull of 80 kN. Find the shear stress in the rivets and the maximum tensile stress in the plates.

$$\text{Shear stress in rivets} = \frac{\text{load}}{\text{area under shear}}$$

$$\text{Load} = 80 \text{ kN} = 80 \times 10^3 \text{ N}$$

$$\text{Area under shear} = 2 \times \frac{\pi}{4} \times 20^2 \qquad = \frac{80 \times 10^3 \times 10^6}{618}$$

$$= 618 \text{ mm}^2 \qquad = \mathbf{129 \cdot 5 \times 10^6 \text{ N/m}^2}$$

$$= 618 \times 10^{-6} \text{ m}^2$$

$$\text{Minimum cross sectional area of plate} = (150 \times 15) - 2(20 \times 15)$$

$$= 2\,250 - 600$$

$$= 1\,650 \text{ mm}^2$$

$$= \mathbf{1\,650 \times 10^{-6} \text{ m}^2}$$

$$\text{Greatest tensile stress} = \frac{\text{load}}{\text{area}}$$

$$= \frac{80 \times 10^3 \times 10^6}{1\,650}$$

$$= \mathbf{48 \cdot 5 \times 10^6 \text{ N/m}^2}$$

EXERCISES

1. A 50 mm diameter rod resists a force of 150 kN. Find the stress in the material.

2. A hollow column of outside diameter 100 mm and inside diameter 75 mm supports a mass of 9 tonnes. Find the stress in the material.

3. If a 50 kN force causes a rod 450 mm long to stretch by 0·51 mm, find the strain in the rod.

4. If a wire 13 m long stretches 6·35 mm when tightened by a winch, find the fractional strain.

5. A load of 30 tonnes causes a mild steel bar, 320 mm long and 12 mm in diameter to stretch 4·1 mm, find the modulus of elasticity of the material.

6. A mild steel bar, 300 mm long, has to carry a load of 27 tonnes. If the maximum permissible extension is 0·75 mm, find the cross-sectional area of the bar. Modulus of elasticity for mild steel 206×10^9 N/m^2.

7. An aluminium tie rod is required to carry a load of 2 500 kg. Find the diameter of the rod if the tensile stress has not to exceed 70 MN/n^2.

   If the rod is 0·9 m long, how much will it stretch under this load? Young's modulus for aluminium—$75·8 \times 10^9$ N/m^2.

8. In a tensile test the following data were obtained for a mild steel bar. Gauge length = 50 mm; Diameter = 15 mm.

Load (N)	4 000	8 000	12 000	16 000	20 000
Extn. (mm)	0·005 63	0·011 26	0·016 89	0·022 52	0·028 15

   Draw a graph of the results and from it calculate the value of Young's modulus of elasticity for the specimen.

9. A power winch is hung from a roof truss by four 75 mm × 75 mm × 10 mm angle irons 1 m long. If the modulus of elasticity of the material is 202×10^9 N/m^2 and the working stress is not to exceed 45×10^6 N/m^2, find

(a) the maximum load which can be lifted (neglect the weight of the winch);

(b) the extension of the angle irons under maximum load.

10. A tie rod of diameter 20 mm is limited to a maximum working load of 5 kN. Find the factor of safety if the ultimate tensile stress of the material is 470 MN/m^2.

11. A mild-steel column of section shown in Fig. 265 is 1·25 m long and has to support a maximum mass of 14 tonnes. If the compression under maximum working load is 0·251 mm, calculate the modulus of elasticity for the material. If the factor of safety for the column is 12, find the ultimate compressive stress of the material.

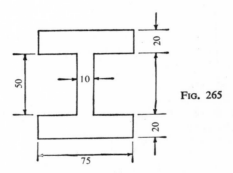

Fig. 265

12. A tow bar consists of a tube of outside diameter 75 mm. If it has to withstand a pull of 120 kN, find the thickness of the metal if the working stress has not to be greater than 60 MN/m^2.

13. A lifting jack has a maximum lift of 300 mm and the diameter of the ram is 75 mm. Find the maximum force the jack may exert if the ram has to have a factor of safety of 7, and the ultimate stress of the metal is 483×10^6 N/m^2.

Find the compression in the ram if the modulus of elasticity is 201×10^9 N/m^2.

14. The cylinder of a double-acting steam engine is 300 mm in diameter, and the piston rod is 750 mm long and 75 mm in diameter. If the working steam pressure is $0·8 \times 10^6$ N/m^2, find the total change in length of the piston rod over two working strokes. Young's modulus for the material is 206×10^9 N/m^2.

15. The two rivets shown in Fig. 266 are subjected to a shear load of 90 kN. Find the shear stress in the rivets and the ultimate shear stress of the material if the factor of safety is 3.

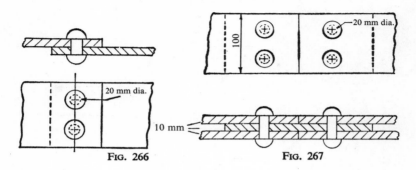

FIG. 266   FIG. 267

16. Fig. 267 shows a riveted joint. If it is subjected to a pull of 100 kN, calculate the shear stress in the rivets and the maximum tensile stress in the centre plate.

17. Fig. 268 shows a knuckle joint. If the pull on the bar is 130 kN, calculate the diameter of the pin required. The ultimate shear stress for the material is 384 MN/m^2 and the factor of safety has to be 8.

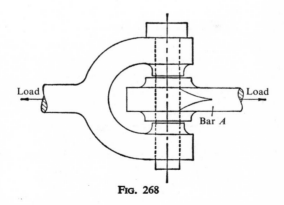

FIG. 268

18. A punching machine is required to punch holes 50 mm square in 10 mm thick mild-steel plate. If the ultimate shear stress of mild steel is 385×10^6 N/m^2, find the force required to drive the punch.

H

19. Find the force necessary to punch a hole 40 mm diameter in a mild-steel plate 5 mm thick if the ultimate shear stress of mild steel is 380 MN/m^2.

Find the compressive stress in the punch.

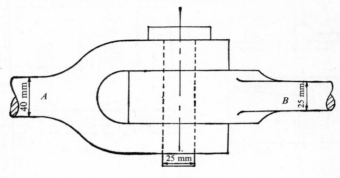

FIG. 269

20. If the knuckle joint shown in Fig. 269 is subjected to a pull of 70 kN, calculate—
    (a) the tensile stress in rods A and B;
    (b) the shear stress in the pin.

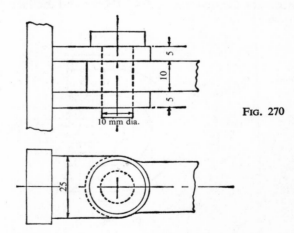

FIG. 270

21. In the swivel joint shown in Fig. 270 the U.T.S. of the material is 430 × 10^6 N/m^2 and the U.S.S. is 370 × 10^6 N/m^2. Calculate the load at which the joint would break.

CHAPTER IX

INTERNAL-COMBUSTION ENGINE

In the internal combustion engine an inflammable mixture of vapour and air is burned in a combustion chamber to produce heat and gas. The heat of combustion causes the gas to expand, but since it is contained in the combustion chamber the volume of the gas remains constant at this instant and a sharp increase in pressure takes place. This high pressure gas is used to push the piston along the cylinder and the linear motion of the piston is converted into rotary motion by the crankshaft.

Different types of fuel may be used such as petrol, diesel oil, paraffin, etc., but the general principles are the same in each engine. The high temperatures generated in these engines necessitates some form of cooling. This is generally achieved by an air or water cooling system.

We will confine our attention to the four-stroke and the two-stroke petrol engines.

Parts of the Engine

1. The carburetter (Fig. 272)

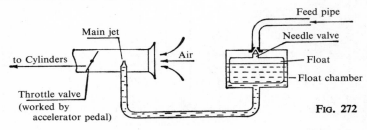

FIG. 272

The petrol pump supplies petrol from the tank to the float chamber via the feed pipe. When the chamber is filled to the correct level the float rises and closes the needle valve thus cutting off the supply.

A pipe connects the bottom of the float chamber to the air intake, and this pipe ends in a fine jet in the air intake tube.

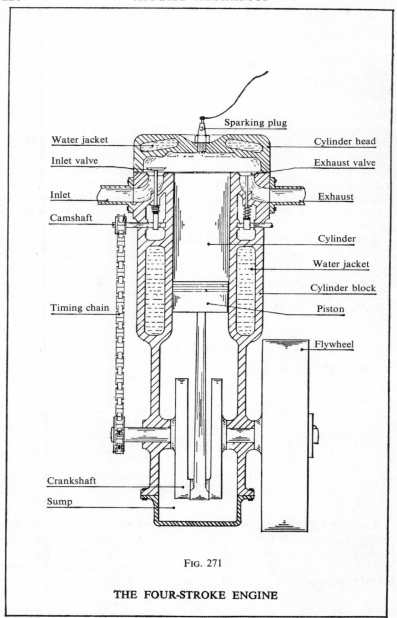

FIG. 271

THE FOUR-STROKE ENGINE

As the piston descends and causes a partial vacuum in the cylinder, air is drawn in and, as the air passes over the jet, it draws petrol from the jet.

The size of the jet determines the ratio of petrol to air in the mixture that enters the cylinder and in most cases the ratio is 15 parts by volume of air to 1 part by volume of petrol vapour.

2. The valves (Fig. 273)

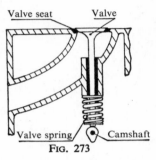

FIG. 273

The valves are generally made of tough nickel steel to enable them to stand up to wear and high temperature. The inlet valve controls the supply of mixture to the cylinder and the exhaust valve controls the flow of exhaust gas from the cylinder. Each valve is opened when required by a cam on the camshaft and is closed again by the valve spring. The camshaft is driven from the crankshaft by the timing chain.

3. The piston and connecting rod (Fig. 274)

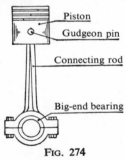

FIG. 274

The piston is generally made of aluminium alloy and the gudgeon pin of mild steel. The piston rings (often 3 in number) are made of spring steel and are set into grooves in the piston. The rings spring outwards against the cylinder wall and prevent the gas from escaping past the piston.

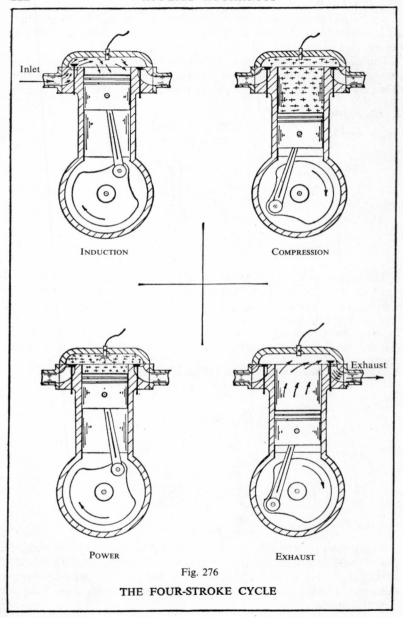

Inlet

INDUCTION

COMPRESSION

POWER

EXHAUST

Exhaust

Fig. 276

THE FOUR-STROKE CYCLE

The connecting rod is made of mild steel and is connected to the crank shaft by the big end bearing. The bearing surface is of white metal, an alloy of tin and lead.

4. The flywheel (Fig. 275)

The flywheel is a heavy metal wheel connected to the crankshaft. When the power stroke turns the engine, it starts the flywheel moving and the inertia of the flywheel carries the piston over the next compression stroke to compress the mixture in the cylinder. Thus the heavy flywheel makes the engine run more smoothly.

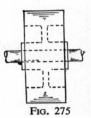

FIG. 275

The four-stroke cycle (Fig. 276)

This cycle of operations takes place over 4 strokes of the piston—i.e. two revolutions of the crankshaft.

The strokes are as follows:—

1. Induction stroke. With the inlet valve open and the exhaust valve shut the piston moves down the cylinder, creating a partial vaccum in the cylinder. A mixture of air and gas (15:1) is drawn in from the carburetter.

2. Compression stroke. With both valves shut the piston moves up the cylinder, compressing the mixture. The mixture is ignited by an electric spark from the sparking plug just before the end of the stroke. The end of this stroke is known as top dead centre (T.D.C.).

3. Power stroke. With both valves shut the hot, high-pressure gas forces the piston down the cylinder. As this happens, the volume of the gas becomes greater, so that the pressure of the gas drops.

4. The exhaust stroke. With the exhaust valve open and the inlet valve shut the piston moves up the cylinder pushing out the exhaust gas and the cycle begins again.

The four-cylinder engine

So far we have examined only a single-cylinder engine. Multicylinder engines work in exactly the same way except that several pistons work on the same crankshaft and fire at different times. This makes the engine run more evenly with a more constant supply of power so that a smaller flywheel is needed.

Fig. 277 shows a four-cylinder engine. The firing order in such an engine is generally 1, 3, 4, 2, or 1, 2, 4, 3.

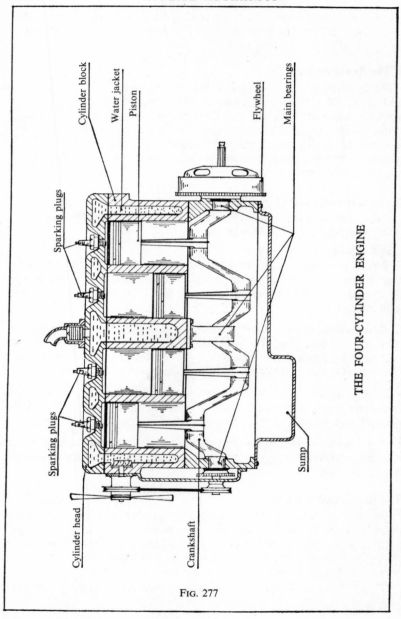

THE FOUR-CYLINDER ENGINE

Sparking plugs

Cylinder block

Water jacket

Piston

Flywheel

Main bearings

Sparking plugs

Cylinder head

Crankshaft

Sump

Fig. 277

Indicator Diagrams

The indicator is a device for measuring the pressure inside the cylinder while the piston is in motion. The diagram will give an idea how it works (Fig. 278).

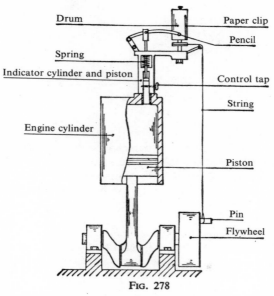

FIG. 278

A piece of paper is wrapped round the drum, and, with the tap between the cylinder and the pressure gauge closed, the engine is allowed to run. On each downward stroke of the pin on the flywheel, the string is pulled and this rotates the drum on its axis. On each upward stroke the drum is returned to its original position by means of a spring. Thus, for every turn of the flywheel, the drum rotates forward and back. As this happens the pencil marks the paper and the length of the pencil mark may be taken to represent the length of the stroke. Since the gauge is working at atmospheric pressure, this line also marks the atmospheric level on the diagram.

When the tap between the pressure gauge and the cylinder is opened the pressure of the gas forces the gauge plunger upwards against the resistance of the indicator spring and the pencil registers the rise on the paper. (The increase in the volume of the gas due to the movement of the gauge plunger is negligible.)

In this way we can get a measure of the pressure in the cylinder at any point on the stroke.

Fig. 279 shows a typical four-stroke indicator diagram for a petrol engine with the atmospheric line *A–L* extended.

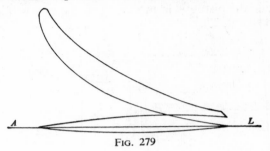

FIG. 279

Indicator springs

The height of the diagram is determined by the stiffness of the indicator spring which is generally expressed in N/m^2 per millimetre of compression. If a spring has a stiffness of 400×10^3 N/m^2 per mm of compression it means that the spring will be compressed by 1 mm for every 400×10^3 N/m^2 pressure in the cylinder.

Interpretation of the diagram

The straight horizontal line *A.L.* on the diagram (Fig. 280) is the atmospheric pressure line—i.e. the normal pressure before the gas is admitted to the gauge. The other lines are as follows:—

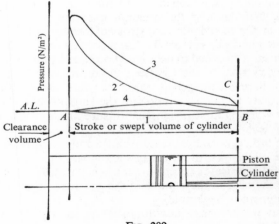

FIG. 280

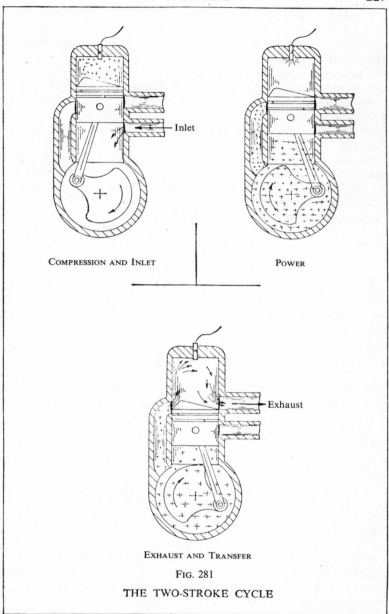

COMPRESSION AND INLET   POWER

EXHAUST AND TRANSFER

FIG. 281

THE TWO-STROKE CYCLE

1. The induction stroke. As the piston moves down the cylinder from A to B, line 1 is drawn on the diagram. Since there is a partial vacuum in the cylinder at this stroke, the lines appears slightly below the atmospheric line.

2. The compression stroke. As the piston moves back up from B to A with both valves closed, the mixture is compressed so that the pressure in the cylinder rises. Just before the end of this stroke—i.e. slightly before "top dead centre"—ignition, accompanied by a sharp rise in pressure, takes place. This is shown by a steep rise on the indicator diagram.

3. Power stroke. As the hot gas pushes the piston down the cylinder again, the volume it occupies becomes greater so that the pressure of the gas falls. Line 3 therefore shows a drop in pressure as the piston moves from A to B. (Exhaust valve opens at c in Fig. 280).

4. The exhaust stroke. The piston again moves up the cylinder from B to A pushing out the exhaust gas. During this stroke the pressure is slightly above atmospheric as shown by line 4 of the diagram.

The Two-Stroke Engine

This is probably the simplest heat engine in common use. Since every second stroke is a working stroke, valves are dispensed with and the gases are admitted and exhausted through holes or **ports**, in the cylinder walls. Fig. 282 shows a two-stroke engine.

1. The compression stroke (Fig. 281). As the piston moves to the top of the cylinder, it causes a partial vacuum in the crank-case so that when the bottom of the piston uncovers the inlet port the mixture from the carburetter is sucked into the crank case. As the piston moves up it also covers the transfer port and the exhaust port, thus trapping some of the mixture in the cylinder and compresses it.

At the top of the stroke the mixture is ignited by an electric spark at the plug.

2. The power stroke. As the hot gas pushes the piston down the cylinder three things happen:

(1) The bottom of the piston closes the inlet port so that as the piston moves further down it compresses the mixture in the crank case.

(2) Near the bottom of the stroke the exhaust port is uncovered allowing the exhaust gas to escape.

(3) The transfer port (on a slightly lower level than the exhaust port) is then uncovered so that the compressed mixture in the crank-case is forced up through the transfer port into the cylinder. The top of the piston is shaped so that the mixture is deflected into the cylinder, thus pushing out any exhaust gases remaining in the cylinder.

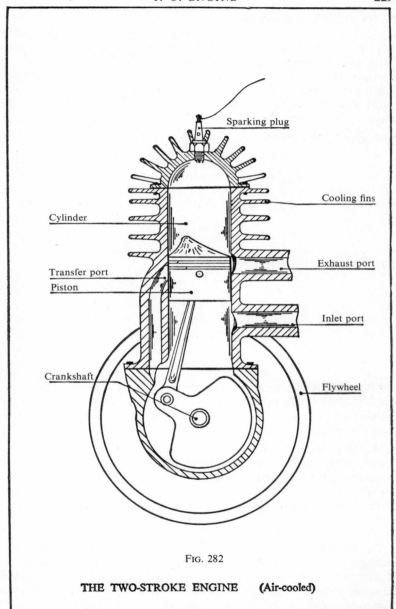

Sparking plug

Cooling fins

Cylinder

Exhaust port

Transfer port

Piston

Inlet port

Crankshaft

Flywheel

FIG. 282

THE TWO-STROKE ENGINE (Air-cooled)

Notes on the two-stroke cycle

(1) This engine has fewer working parts than the four-stroke engine since ports replace valves, camshaft and timing mechanism.

(2) Generally speaking, the engine is not as efficient as the four-stroke engine since the scavenging power (removal of the exhaust gas) is not so definite as that of the four-stroke engine.

(3) The big end bearing and the cylinder walls are lubricated by oil mixed with the petrol.

Indicator diagram for the two-stroke cycle (Fig. 283)

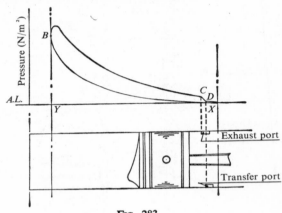

FIG. 283

Compression stroke. As the piston moves from X to Y it covers the transfer and exhaust ports and traps the mixture in the cylinder. As the piston moves to the top of the cylinder (Y) the mixture is compressed as shown by line XB in the diagram. The mixture is fired at B.

Working stroke. As the piston moves down the cylinder from Y to X the gas expands and the pressure drops. At point C the exhaust port is uncovered and a sharp fall in pressure occurs to point D. The transfer port is then uncovered and a new charge of the mixture is forced from the crank-case into the cylinder and the cycle begins again.

Mean effective pressure (m.e.p.)

The diagram (Fig. 284) shows a typical two-stroke cycle, showing the pressure on the piston at every point on its travel. During the upstroke (1) the piston compresses the mixture—i.e. the piston does work on the mixture. When the piston is on the downstroke the gas pushes the piston—i.e. the gas does work on the piston.

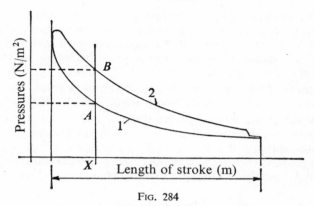

FIG. 284

On the upstroke the pressure exerted by the piston on the mixture when the piston is at point X will be A N/m². On the downstroke when the piston is again at point X the pressure exerted on the piston by the gas will be B N/m², so that the effective pressure exerted on the piston will be $(B—A)$ N/m² at this point. Similarly we may find the effective pressure on the piston at any other point on its travel by subtracting the pressure on line 1 from the pressure on line 2. From this we see that the height of the diagram at any point measures the effective pressure at that point.

The height of the diagram varies throughout its length showing that the effective pressure is different at different points in the stroke. We require to find a mean value for this varying effective pressure and this is done by applying the "mid-ordinate rule".

The mid-ordinate rule

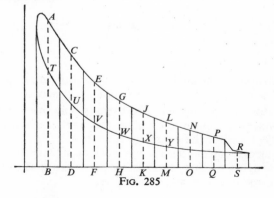

FIG. 285

Divide the diagram (Fig. 285) into a convenient number of strips of equal width, and through each strip erect the mid-ordinates AB, CD, EF, etc. Measure the height of the diagram on each mid-ordinate, i.e. TA, UC, VE, etc., and find the mean height—this height, to scale, gives the mean effective pressure.

This mean effective pressure (m.e.p.) can be taken as the average pressure which acts throughout the whole length of the working stroke.

When using this method to determine m.e.p. it will be convenient to keep the diagram dimensions in millimetres because as you will remember, spring stiffness is normally stated in N/mm^2 per millimetre of compression. Therefore when the height of the diagram is measured in mm and multiplied by the spring stiffness the m.e.p. is found in N/m^2.

Indicated power

Knowing the mean effective pressure we can calculate the power developed in the cylinder by the gas, i.e. the indicated power.

Let the mean effective pressure $= P \ N/m^2$

Length of piston stroke $= L$ m

Area of top of piston $= A$ m^2

Number of working strokes/second $= n$

Force acting on the piston = pressure × area

$= P \times A$ newtons

Work done during 1 working stroke = force × distance

$= PA \times L$ joules

Work done per second $= PAL \times n$ joules

Indicated power = PLAn watts

Notes

(1) If the speed of the engine is given in rev/min this must be divided by 60 to obtain the number of revolutions per second.

(2) In a four-stroke engine, since there is only one working stroke for every two revolutions of the engine, the number of working strokes per second = speed of the engine in rev/sec ÷ 2.

In a two-stroke engine there is one working stroke for every revolution of the engine so that the number of working strokes/second is equal to the speed of the engine in rev/sec.

(3) So far we have considered only a single cylinder. In a multi-cylinder engine the number of working strokes for one cylinder must be multiplied by the number of cylinders.

(4) In the design and manufacture of engines, dimensions are nearly always stated in millimetres. It is possible to calculate the power using millimetres but it is normally better to convert all dimensions into metres.

Area of the indicator diagram

As an alternative to using the mid-ordinate rule to find the m.e.p., the area enclosed by the indicator diagram can be measured using a planimeter (an instrument for measuring the area of irregular plane figures) and since the length of the diagram can be measured, we can find the mean height of the diagram.

$$\text{Mean height (mm)} = \frac{\text{area of diagram (mm}^2)}{\text{length (mm)}}$$

If the diagram dimensions are in mm then the mean height in mm may be used with the spring stiffness N/mm^2 per millimetre of compression to calculate the mean effective pressure.

$$\text{m.e.p. (N/m}^2) = \text{mean height (mm)} \times \text{spring stiffness (N/m}^2/\text{mm)}$$

Example 1

In an I.C. engine test using an indicator of spring stiffness 20×10^3 $N/m^2/mm$ it was found that the diagram had an area of 1 550 mm^2 and a length of 71 mm. Calculate the mean effective pressure in the cylinder.

$$\text{Area of diagram} = \text{length} \times \text{mean height}$$

$$\text{Mean height} = \frac{\text{area}}{\text{length}}$$

$$= \frac{1\,550}{71}$$

$$= \mathbf{21 \cdot 8 \text{ mm}}$$

Since the spring stiffness is 20×10^3 $N/m^2/mm$,

$$\text{m.e.p.} = \text{mean height of the diagram} \times \text{spring stiffness}$$

$$= 21 \cdot 8 \times 20 \times 10^3$$

$$= \mathbf{436 \times 10^3 \text{ N/m}^2}$$

Example 2

Calculate the indicated power of a 4-cylinder engine working on the four-stroke cycle when it runs at a speed of 1 700 rev/min. The pistons are 100 mm in diameter, the length of stroke is 175 mm, and the mean effective pressure is 0·58 MN/m².

Mean effective pressure$(P) = 0·58$ MN/m² $= 0·58 \times 10^6$ N/m²

$$\text{Length of stroke } (L) = 175 \text{ mm}$$
$$= 0·175 \text{ m}$$

$$\text{Area of piston } (A) = \frac{\pi D^2}{4}$$

$$= \frac{\pi}{4} \times 100^2$$

$$= 7\,850 \text{ mm}^2 = 7\,850 \times 10^{-6} \text{ m}^2$$

Number of working strokes per second $(n) = \dfrac{1\,700}{2 \times 60} \times 4$

$$= 56·7$$

$$\text{Indicated power} = PLAn$$

$$= 0·58 \times 10^6 \times 0·175 \times 7\,850 \times 10^6 \times 56·7$$

$$= 0·58 \times 0·175 \times 7\,850 \times 56·7$$

$$= 45\,000 \text{ W}$$

$$= \mathbf{45\ kW}$$

Brake Power

From the indicator diagram and the dimensions of the engine we can calculate the indicated power of the engine. This is the power that would be obtained if all the energy developed in the cylinder could be delivered as useful work. Unfortunately much of this energy is used up in overcoming friction between the piston and the cylinder walls and in the bearings so that the power delivered by the engine to perform useful work is less than the indicated power.

In order to test the engine we make it drive a wheel against the action of a brake and as we can calculate the power absorbed by the brake (see friction) we can calculate the **brake power** (B.P.) of the engine, i.e. the power delivered by the engine to do useful work.

We have seen from our study of friction that the power absorbed by a brake

$$= 2\pi nT \quad \text{W}$$

where $n =$ speed of the wheel in rev/s

$T =$ braking torque in Nm.

Brake Tests

1. The Prony brake

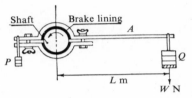

FIG. 286

The brake consists of a metal gland lined on the inside with brake lining. The gland has a long arm and a short arm as shown (Fig. 286). Small masses are added at P so that this weight balances the weight of arm A and the gland is tightened to a suitable degree on the shaft.

The engine is started and made to turn the shaft. The friction between the gland and the shaft tends to rotate the brake but this is prevented by suitable masses hung at Q to give a force of W newtons so that the arm remains horizontal. In this state the friction torque on the shaft is balanced by the moment of W about the centre of the shaft.

The moment of W is found $(W \times L)$; this gives the friction torque and knowing the friction torque we can calculate the power absorbed by the brake.

$$\text{B.P.} = 2\pi nT$$

2. The rope brake

The rope, in the form of a loop, is wound round the flywheel as shown in Fig. 287. One end of the rope is fixed to a spring balance and a mass of weight W, the "dead load", is hung at the free end. Thus the rope is held in tension and exerts a pressure on the flywheel.

The engine under test is started and made to drive the flywheel against the friction between the wheel and the rope. Masses are added or subtracted at the dead load until the spring balance gives a

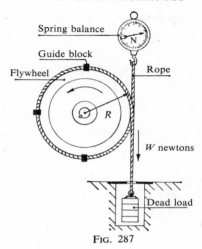

Spring balance

Guide block

Flywheel

Rope

R

W newtons

Dead load

FIG. 287

reasonable reading. The engine is allowed to run for some time until the spring balance settles at a steady reading. This reading is noted and the value of W calculated.

Let the "dead load" $= W$ N

Spring balance reading $= S$ N

$\therefore$ Effective load $= (W—S)$ N

Radius of flywheel $= R$ m

Radius of the rope $= r$ m

$\therefore$ Effective radius $= (R + r)$ m

Friction torque $= T$ Nm

Engine speed $= n$ rev/s

As the wheel rotates the load is balanced by the friction of the rope on the wheel; i.e. the moment of the load about the centre of the wheel $=$ friction torque.

$$(W - S)(R + r) = T$$

Power absorbed at a brake $= 2\pi nT$

$$= 2\pi n(W - S)(R + r)$$

Mechanical efficiency

Since the indicated power is the power developed in the cylinder and the brake power is the actual power delivered by the engine, the difference is due to mechanical losses in the engine so that

Mechanical efficiency of the engine $= \dfrac{\text{power delivered by the engine}}{\text{power developed in the cylinder}}$

$$= \frac{\text{B.P.}}{\text{I.P.}}$$

Notes

(1) The brake power will always be less than the indicated power so the efficiency is always a fraction. It may also be expressed as a percentage

$$\text{Mechanical efficiency} = \frac{\text{B.P.}}{\text{I.P.}} \times 100$$

(2) The power lost in friction may be calculated by subtracting the brake power from the indicated power

$$\text{Power lost in friction} = \text{I.P.} - \text{B.P.}$$

Example

A four-cylinder internal-combustion engine, working on the four-stroke cycle has cylinders of 75 mm bore and stroke length 125 mm. The following results were obtained under test.

$$\text{Speed of the engine} = 2\,250 \text{ rev/min}$$

$$\text{Mean effective pressure} = 580 \times 10^3 \text{ N/m}^2$$

$$\text{Brake torque} = 60 \text{ Nm}$$

Calculate the mechanical efficiency of the engine.

$$\text{Mean effective pressure } (P) = 580 \times 10^3 \text{ N/m}^2$$

$$\text{Length of stroke } (L) = 125 \text{ mm}$$

$$= 0 \cdot 125 \text{ m}$$

$$\text{Area of piston } (A) = \frac{\pi D^2}{4}$$

$$= \frac{3 \cdot 14}{4} \times 75^2$$

$$= 4\,418 \text{ mm}^2 = 4\,418 \times 10^{-6} \text{ m}^2$$

Number of working strokes/second $(n) = \dfrac{2\,250}{2 \times 60} \times 4$

$$= 75$$

$$\text{Indicated power} = PLAn$$
$$= 580 \times 10^3 \times 0.125 \times 4\,418 \times 10^{-6} \times 75$$
$$= 580 \times 0.125 \times 4\,418 \times 75 \times 10^3$$
$$= \mathbf{2\,400\ W}$$

$$\text{Brake power} = 2\pi nT$$

where n = speed of the engine in rev/sec

and T = friction torque in Nm

$$= 2 \times 3.14 \times 37.5 \times 60$$
$$= \mathbf{14\,120\ W}$$

$$\text{Mechanical efficiency} = \frac{\text{B.P.}}{\text{I.P.}} \times 100$$
$$\frac{14\,120}{24\,000} \times 100$$
$$= \mathbf{58.8\,\%}$$

EXERCISES

1. An internal-combustion engine has a piston 100 mm in diameter and a stroke length of 175 mm. Find the amount of work done during one working stroke if the mean effective pressure is 0.82×10^6 N/m².

2. An engine is required to do 600 J work during one working stroke. If the m.e.p. is 0.54×10^6 N/m² and the length of stroke 150 mm find the diameter of piston necessary.

3. The following information was obtained from an engine test on a two-stroke, single-cylinder engine:—
   Cross-sectional area of piston = 4 500 mm²
   Length of stroke = 125 mm
   Speed of the engine = 2 200 rev/min
   Mean effective pressure = 0.58×10^6 N/m²
   Calculate the indicated power of the engine.

4. A four-cylinder, four-stroke engine is required to develop 35 kW at 1 500 rev/min. If the length of stroke is 175 mm and the m.e.p. is 0.45×10^6 N/m² calculate the diameter of the pistons required.

5. A two-cylinder, four-stroke, oil engine develops 12 kW at 2 000 rev/min. If the piston diameter is 75 mm and the length of stroke 140 mm, find the m.e.p.

6. The indicator diagram of an engine is found to have an area of 933 mm². If the length of the diagram is 66 mm and the spring stiffness of the indicator is 31.5×10^3 N/m² per mm of compression, find the m.e.p. of the engine.

7. In a rope brake test on a steam engine the following results were obtained:—

$$\text{Diameter of flywheel} = 1.25 \text{ m}$$
$$\text{Speed of flywheel} = 230 \text{ rev/min}$$
$$\text{Diameter of rope} = 20 \text{ mm}$$
$$\text{Dead load} = 70 \text{ kg}$$
$$\text{Spring balance reading} = 54 \text{ N}$$

Find the brake power of the engine.

8. In a brake test the following results were obtained from a two-cylinder, four-stroke, oil engine:—

$$\text{Area of piston} = 4\,250 \text{ mm}^2$$
$$\text{Length of stroke} = 180 \text{ mm}$$
$$\text{M.e.p.} = 0.52 \times 10^6 \text{ N/m}^2$$
$$\text{Speed} = 1\,800 \text{ rev/min}$$
$$\text{Diameter of flywheel} = 0.5 \text{ m}$$
$$\text{Diameter of rope} = 25 \text{ mm}$$
$$\text{Dead load} = 21 \text{ kg}$$
$$\text{S.B.R.} = 56 \text{ N}$$

Calculate the I.P., B.P., and mechanical efficiency of the engine.

9. A six-cylinder, two-stroke marine engine yielded the following results:—

$$\text{M.e.p.} = 0.56 \times 10^6 \text{ N/m}^2$$
$$\text{Length of stroke} = 200 \text{ mm}$$
$$\text{Area of piston} = 8\,500 \text{ mm}^2$$
$$\text{Speed} = 1\,200 \text{ rev/min}$$
$$\text{Diameter of flywheel} = 0.7 \text{ m}$$
$$\text{Diameter of rope} = 25 \text{ mm}$$
$$\text{Dead load} = 175 \text{ kg}$$
$$\text{S.B.R.} = 65 \text{ N}$$

Find the I.P., B.P., and mechanical efficiency of the engine.

10. On a four-stroke, four-cylinder petrol engine the following results were obtained under test :—

$$\text{Indicator spring stiffness} = 31\cdot5 \times 10^3 \text{ N/m}^2\text{/mm}$$
$$\text{Area of indicator diagram} = 1\,550 \text{ mm}^2$$
$$\text{Length of indicator diagram} = 100 \text{ mm}$$
$$\text{Area of piston} = 4\,500 \text{ mm}^2$$
$$\text{Length of stroke} = 150 \text{ mm}$$
$$\text{Speed} = 1\,700 \text{ rev/min}$$
$$\text{Diameter of flywheel} = 400 \text{ mm}$$
$$\text{Diameter of rope} = 12 \text{ mm}$$
$$\text{Dead load} = 45 \text{ kg}$$
$$\text{Spring balance reading} = 122 \text{ N}$$

Calculate the mechanical efficiency of the engine.

ANSWERS

FORCES
Chapter I, Page 36

1. 528 N, 432 N.
2. 566 N, 284 N.
3. 168 N, 21°.
4. 161 N.
5. 26·6 N.
6. 1 133 N, 2 266 N.
7. 9 280 N, 5 070 N.
8. 25° 30′, 49°.
9. 4 225 N, 1 550 N.
10. $Rw = 373$ N, $Rg = 961$N at 67·5°
11. 1 225 N, 2 520 N at 62°.
12. 50 N, 66 N, 58 N.
13. 19·3 kg, 1 715 N.
14. 10·8 N at 25° to 8 N force.
15. 10 200 N.
16.′ 147·5 N.
17. 7 100 N, 4 200 N.
18. 740 N.
19. 14·3 N, 11·2 N at 243°.
20. 96·5 N, 100°, 0·355 m from A.
21. 57 N, 225°, 0·275 m from A.
22. 21·75 N, 10·14 N.
23. 283 N.
24. 169·6 N.
25. 109·7 N.
26. 17 N at 28° 6′ to 15 N force.
27. 98·5 N at 23° 57′ off course.
28. 236 N.
29. 33 746 N, 44 145 N.
30. 416 N.
31. No answer.
32. 4·05 N 5°.
33. $PQ = 24$ N, $QS = 27·4$ N.
34. 114·3 kN, 22·1 kN.
35. 11 N at 129°.
36. 205 N, 88°.
37. 15·6 N at 310°.

MOMENTS
Chapter II, Page 61

1. 125 mm.
2. 250 N.
3. 18·5 kg, 540 N.
4. 106·67 N.
5. 6·79 m from left.
6. $R_1 = 178·5$ N, $R_2 = 301·5$ N.
7. $Ra = 2 337·5$ N, $Rb = 1 507·4$ N.
8. $A = 11 308$ kg, $B = 11 232$ kg.
9. $S_1 = 1 800$ N, $S_2 = 2 400$ N.
10. 589·2 N.
11. (a) 2 m, (b) $58·86 \times 10^6$ N, (c) to right.
12. 2 257 N, 5 100 N.
13. $25·5 \times 10^3$ N.
14. 831·4 N.
15. 78 N.
16. 94 N.
17. 385·2 N.
18. $T_1 = 2·88 \times 10^3$ N, $T_2 = 2·59 \times 10^3$ N.

CENTRE OF GRAVITY
Chapter III, Page 79

1. (a) 136·8 mm →
   (c) 2·5 m ↑ 0·975 m →
   (e) 65 mm ↑ 55 mm →
   (g) 0·59 m →
   (i) 71·0 mm →
   (k) 50 mm →
   (b) 124·2 mm →
   (d) 2·213 m ↑ 0·907 m →
   (f) 51·6 mm ↑ 88·4 mm →
   (h) 83·6 mm ↑ 106·4 mm →
   (j) 16·28 mm ↑ 78·6 mm →
2. 4·637 m from left, 22 610 N.
3. 618 mm above ground level.
4. 215 mm from left.

FRAMES *Chapter IV, Page* 90

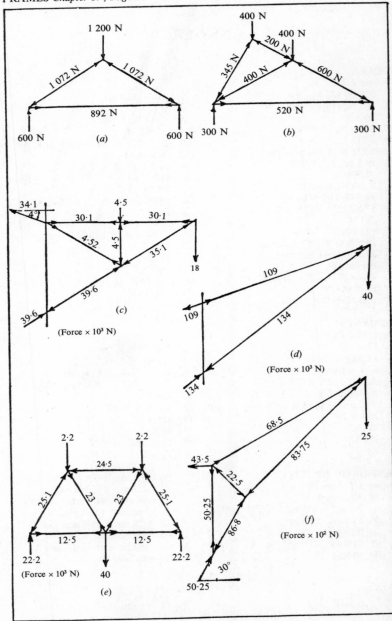

243

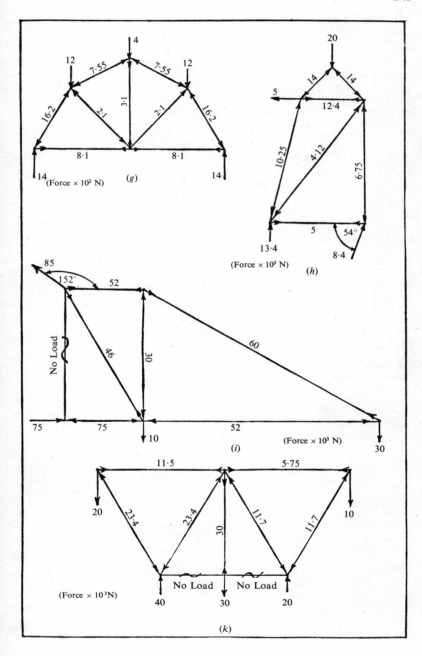

(Force × 10² N) (g)

(Force × 10³ N) (h)

(i) (Force × 10³ N)

(Force × 10³ N)

(k)

FRICTION
Chapter V, Page 114

1. 0·081 5.
3. 10·3 N.
5. 140 N.
7. 48·1 N.
9. (*a*) 31·4 N, (*b*) 48·2 N.
11. 10 700 N.
13. 389 N.
15. 5·4 Nm.
17. 31·2 × 10⁻³ Nm.

2. 0·208.
4. 70 N.
6. 145 N.
8. 632 N.
10. 13° 42′.
12. 70 N/tonne.
14. 8·46 × 10⁶ N.
16. 6·24 Nm.
18. 0·114 5.

WORK, ENERGY, POWER
Chapter VI, Page 140

1. 135 J.
3. 7 357 J.
5. 1 348·8 J.
7. 736 W.
9. 1·25 kW.
11. 95 N/tonne.
13. 121 W.
15. 5·16 kW.
17. 546 000 J.
19. 1.58 min (1 min 34 s).
21. 56·25 J.
23. 0·5 W.
25. 7·03 kW, 115 mm.
27. 101 mm.
29. 5·1 × 10³ N.

2. 5 000 J.
4. 184 × 10³ J.
6. 0·612 m³.
8. 61·3 kW.
10. 72 km/h.
12. 5·81 kW.
14. 5·52 kW.
16. 1 267 J.
18. 297·5 × 10³ J.
20. 146 × 10³ J.
22. 5·98 J.
24. (*a*) 360 rev/min, (*b*) 349 rev/min.
26. 1 092 N, 2 730 N.
28. 21 mm.
30. 4·67 kW.

MACHINES
Chapter VII, Page 186

1. 9·81.
3. 400 mm.
5. 888·8 N.
7. 24, 365·5 kg.
9. 2, anticlockwise.

2. 5·71.
4. (1) 100 J, (2) 68·67 J, (3) 0·686 7.
6. 7·64 kg.
8. 503 N.
10.

Driver	20	35	40	50
	4/7	7/4	2/1	5/2
	1/2	7/8	8/7	10/7
	2/5	7/10	4/5	5/4

11. 120, 50 rev/min.
13. 30.
15. 600 mm, 72 m.
17. 40.
19. (1) 65·6, (2) 143·2.
21.

	V.R.	Effort
(*a*)	106·67	5·75 N.
(*b*)	53·33	11·5 N.
(*c*)	35·55	17·25 N.

23. 0·625 min (37·5 s).

12. 50 rev/min.
14. 750 N.
16. 400 mm (radius).
18. 75·4 kg, (1) 49·3, (2) 0·448, (3) 0·455.
20. 10·25 mm.
22. $P = 0·18L + 9·53$, 0·308, 0·327.
24. $P = 0·048L + 3$, 0·440.

MATERIALS
Chapter VIII, Page 215

1. 76.4×10^6 N/m^2
3. 0.001 13.
5. 203×10^9 N/m^2.
7. 21.1 mm, 0.831 mm.
9. 25.7×10^3 kg, 0.22 mm.
11. 195×10^9 N/m^2, 471×10^6 N/m^2.
13. 304 kN, 0.103 mm.
15. $1\,404 \times 10^6$ N/m^2, $4\,212 \times 10^6$ N/m^2.
17. 41.5 mm.
19. 239×10^3 N, 190×10^6 N/m^2.
21. 58.2×10^3 N will fail in shear.

2. 25.7×10^6 N/m^2.
4. 0.000 488.
6. 25.4 mm.
8. 201×10^9 N/m^2.
10. 7.4.
12. 9.8 mm.
14. 0.090 3 mm.
16. 781×10^6 N/m^2, $1\,625 \times 10^6$ N/m^2.
18. 770×10^3 N.
20. (a) 55.75×10^6 N/m^2.
 142×10^6 N/m^2.
 (b) 71.3×10^6 N/m^2.

ENGINES
Chapter IX, Page 238

1. 1 127 J.
3. 11.97 kW.
5. 0.583×10^6 N/m^2.
7. 9.685 kW.
9. 114.3 kW, 75 kW, 65.8%.

2. 97 mm.
4. 106.4 mm diameter.
6. 0.445×10^6 N/m^2.
8. 11.93 kW, 7.44 kW, 62.33%.
10. 18.65 kW, 11.68 kW, 62.54%.

INDEX